EAT UP
SLIM DOWN

ANNUAL
RECIPES

2007

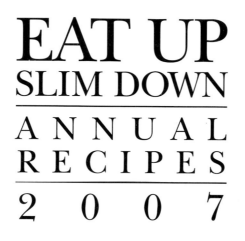

EAT UP
SLIM DOWN
ANNUAL
RECIPES
2 0 0 7

150 Simply Delicious Recipes
for Permanent Weight Loss

RODALE

© 2007 by Rodale Inc.

All rights reserved. No part of this publication may be reproduced or transmitted in any form or by any means, electronic or mechanical, including photocopying, recording, or any other information storage and retrieval system, without the written permission of the publisher.

Eat Up Slim Down is a trademark and *Prevention* is a registered trademark of Rodale Inc.

Printed in the United States of America

Rodale Inc. makes every effort to use acid-free ∞, recycled paper ♲.

Portions of this book have been adapted from material that has appeared in *Prevention* magazine and in the Rodale book entitled *Body for Life for Women*, by Pamela Peeke, MD, MPH, FACP.

Book design by Kristen Morgan Downey

Interior and cover photography credits are on page 251.

Front cover recipe: Caramel Flan with Fresh Fruit (page 225)

ISBN-13 978-1-59486-537-4
ISBN-10 1-59486-537-X

2 4 6 8 10 9 7 5 3 1   hardcover

We inspire and enable people to improve their lives and the world around them

For more of our products visit **rodalestore.com** or call 800-848-4735

Contents

Special Thanks

In grateful appreciation to all the supporters and sponsors of the Eat Up Slim Down Recipe Sweepstakes, we would like to thank . . .

The companies that so generously provided the terrific prizes for the sweepstakes: BonJour, Capresso, Chantal, Hearthware, Leifheit, Soehnle, and Wusthof-Trident.

The product representatives who were so generous with their time and talents: American Spoon Foods; Compari tomatoes; Crum Creek Mills; Cuisinart; Heinz; King Arthur Flour; Maya Kaimal; Melissa's/World Variety Produce, Inc.; Pepperidge Farm; Pom Wonderful; Quaker Oats; RiceSelect; and Yoplait.

And sincere, heartfelt thanks . . .

. . . to all the readers of www.eatupslimdown.com and www.prevention.com who were kind enough to share their delicious recipes, clever tips, and inspiring stories of weight-loss success for this book. We salute you and wish you continued success.

. . . to the seven weight-loss winners who shared their stories of success with us in personal profiles: Kim Bensen, Jackie Dornblaser, Evelyn Gross, Lauren Huff, Carrie Nelson, Evia Nelson, and Jen Sall.

Acknowledgments

A very special thank you to everyone who had a hand in creating
Eat Up Slim Down Annual Recipes 2007.

Carol Angstadt
Miriam Backes
Katie Becker
JoAnn Brader
Tara Chu
Christine Detris
Kristen Morgan Downey
Marilyn Hauptly
Joely Johnson
Fran Kriebel
Mitch Mandel
Lonnie McDonald
Amy McKenzie
Joan Parkin
Stacy Petrovich
Miriam Rubin
Sharon Sanders
Kimberly Tweed
Diane Vezza
Emily Williams
Shannon Yeakel
Shea Zukowski

Contributors

This book is a compilation of the delicious and creative recipes sent to us by weight-loss winners across the United States, and even beyond. The number of recipes we received was so great, it was a difficult task choosing 150. But after a careful selection process, we managed to whittle it down. Here are this year's recipe contributors. We salute their innovative efforts in the kitchen, and hope you'll enjoy eating up and slimming down with their recipes!

Name and Residence	Recipe	Page
Shirley Hill, Chatham, Ontario, Canada	Fall Squash Soup	71
Ben Hill, Dresden, Ontario, Canada	Fruity-Cheesy Pizza	237
Nadine Hill, Dresden, Ontario, Canada	Rice Crispy Cake	241
Audra Hungate, Kearney, Missouri	Green Beans with Roasted Red Peppers	119
Dawn Hurtado, Vandalia, Illinois	Breakfast Eggs	208
Ronda Ireland, Arcade, New York	Simply Done Veggies	109
Ed Izsak, Kipling, Saskatchewan, Canada	Cream of Cabbage Soup	63
Carolyn Jackson, Rochester, New York	Fruity Yogurt	220
Elizabeth Janelle, Arlington, Virginia	Maple-Glazed Asian Salmon Salad	58
Karen Johnson, Sarnia, Ontario, Canada	Healthy Bean Salad	57
Nikki Johnson, Fridley, Minnesota	Lime and Tortilla Soup	74
Maryellen Kerin, Rockaway, New Jersey	Egg and Cucumber–Salad Sandwiches	95
Lyn King, Leavenworth, Kansas	Light and Creamy Fettuccine with Asparagus	137
Michelle King, St. George, Nebraska	Slim Cherry Cheesecake	226
Barbara Kohn, Whitewater, Wisconsin	Chocolate Cheesecake	242
Carol Lambert, Cincinnati, Ohio	Mustard Salad Dressing	62
Mary LaSee, Naples, Florida	Chocolate Oatmeal	202
Melinda Lauck, El Paso, Texas	Beef Stew on Toast	182
Pamela Lebi, Tucson, Arizona	Skillet Sweet Potatoes	114
	Pammy's Curry in a Hurry!	189
Mimi Lenio, Palm Coast, Florida	The Best Black Bean–Turkey Chili	64
Melinda Li, Washington, D.C.	Spicy Olive Pasta	134
Stephanie Little, Cypress, Texas	Southwestern Shrimp and Rice Skillet	148
	Peach Breakfast Parfait	201
Christi Long, Cleveland, Tennessee	Smoked Turkey Sausage Rigatoni	177
Lori Lovesky, Sarasota, Florida	Breakfast Smoothie	215
Rupali Lubchansky, North Brunswick, New Jersey	Healthy and Hearty Pasta	175
Karen MacKenzie, Kennebunk, Maine	Oven-Roasted Sweet Potatoes	115
Laura Magill, Goodwood, Ontario, Canada	Bananas Canadienne	233
Armena Marie, Locust Grove, Virginia	Amy's Apple Sandwiches	101
	Amazing Salad Sandwiches	96
Elizabeth Martlock, Jim Thorpe, Pennsylvania	Prosciutto-Grilled Asparagus	118
	Parmesan Pita Chips with Hummus	89
	Whole Wheat Linguine with Creamy Tomato-Pesto Sauce	133

Name and Residence	Recipe	Page
Elizabeth Martlock, Jim Thorpe, Pennsylvania	Crab-Stuffed Tilapia with Tarragon "Cream" Sauce	155
	Grilled Chicken with Red Onion Confit	161
Elena Martlock, Bethlehem, Pennsylvania	Spaghetti Pie	186
Susan McClure, Edmonton, Alberta, Canada	Breakfast Berry Smoothie	214
Lonnie McDonald, Sellersville, Pennsylvania	Swiss Steak	184
	Garlic Pork	190
	Sausage and Egg Overnight Casserole	204
Saundra McKenzie, Phoenix, Arizona	Tuscan Country Chicken	171
Judith Michalski, Rochester Hills, Michigan	Chocolate Dreams	244
	Great Low-Cal Oatmeal Cookies	221
Jan Miller, Hillsborough, New Jersey	Honey-Apple Chicken	172
Rosalyn Minassian, Burlington, Massachusetts	Bulgur Salad	42
Cindy Miner, Sioux Falls, South Dakota	Diet Pizzas	106
Sharon Murphy, Chicago, Illinois	Southwest Chicken Soup	65
Maya Nair, Alpharetta, Georgia	Tofu-Spinach Wrap	102
Christie Neal, Auburn, Washington	Grilled Cilantro-Lime Chicken	164
Lori Rael Northon, Auburn, Washington	Summer Cooler Fruit Pie	236
Julie Nusbaum, Hamilton, Indiana	Raisin Bran Muffins	199
Irene O'Donnell, Moline, Illinois	Cranberry-Almond Jam	85
Margaly Patterson, Miami, Florida	Gingered Salsa	80
	"Wake Up and Sing" Drink	212
Angelica Persson, Loxley, Alabama	Zesty Summer Salad	40
Lynn Phillips, Macungie, Pennsylvania	Easy Asparagus Omelet	206
Lynne Pizette, Hopkinton, Massachusetts	Broiled Shrimp Scampi	147
Jody Popik, Twinsburg, Ohio	Black Bean Soup	75
Gina Powell, Las Vegas, Nevada	Low-Fat Spinach Dip	92
Karen Preston, Smithville, Ontario, Canada	Karen's Rice	183
David Purdy, Sacramento, California	Caramel Flan with Fresh Fruit	225
Vaishali Ramjee, Winter Garden, Florida	Tofu Curry	141
Melissa Resnick, Furlong, Pennsylvania	Taco Spread	94
Renee Rewiski, Hawthorne, New Jersey	Grilled Eggplant Parmesan	138
Ann Rhew, Floresville, Texas	Chile-Corn Casserole	127
Morgan Riggan, Nanaimo, British Columbia, Canada	Spicy Tuna Salad Mix	45
	Pita Pocket Pizzas	104
	Easy Low-Cal Dressing or Dip	84

Introduction

Welcome to the sixth edition of *Eat Up Slim Down*, the weight-loss cookbook created by *you* and for *you*. You are truly the star of this year's volume. As always, we rely upon the latest scientific and medical research to bring you up-to-date weight-loss information and solutions. This year, the latest breakthrough is all about tailoring diet and exercise to the needs of the individual—you.

Current weight-loss research reveals that all the major diet programs deliver about the same amount of weight loss, and no single plan is significantly more healthy—or unhealthy—than the rest. But just as not all calories are created equal, neither are all dieters. Weight loss finally works for good when it fits *your* personality, *your* lifestyle, and *your* taste in food.

We'll assist you in determining your special needs and then help in developing a plan to fit these changes into your life. We have the strategies and recipes to support you every step of the way. In the following chapters, we'll share the latest smart tactics for meeting "real-world" dieting and exercise challenges with ease. And, with Now the Magic Happens weight-loss tips (page 31), we'll be with you every month of the year with smart suggestions to help you stay on course. The satisfying recipes, all from real dieters just like you, will satisfy your sensual needs for real food as they nourish your success.

This 2007 edition is all about a new you in the real world!

The Year
of a New You!

Next Monday . . . after the holidays . . . after my birthday party . . . when it's closer to bathing suit season . . . when I finish the last Dove Bar in the freezer . . . as soon as this crunch is over at work.

Like most people thinking about dieting, you probably have a "start time" in mind, a day when you're sure you'll be absolutely ready to dive in. But is that "ready" enough to guarantee success?

"A lot of people say, 'I'm ready to take off the pounds,' but that's a lot different from being willing to make the lifestyle changes necessary to actually lose the weight," says John Jakicic, PhD, director of the Physical Activity and Weight Management Research Center at the University of Pittsburgh. The difference between the two is the difference between dropping those pounds, or struggling—and not succeeding.

Test Your Readiness

Before you take the leap, make sure there's a safety net to catch you. The answers to our self-analysis questionnaire will give you a better idea of whether you're prepared to face the challenges ahead of you. And if you're not, we'll equip you with the insights you need to make sure you're truly good to go.

1. **Your last attempt to lose weight was:**

a. A disaster. You couldn't stick with the diet for more than a few days, so you'll never try that plan again.

WHAT MOVES YOU?

The feminine impulse to nurture can be turned inward and you can become your own best caregiver, says Pamela Peeke, MD, MPH, FACP, clinical assistant professor of medicine at the University of Maryland School of Medicine and author of *Body for Life for Women*.

Because the idea of "getting healthy" often isn't enough motivation for most people to initiate and maintain successful weight loss, she recommends creating a Motivational Target—like an archery target with inner and outer rings—to help better understand your feelings. The outer rings include the reasons you feel obligated to make a change, such as your health, and the inner rings are the deeply personal, maybe even hidden, reasons that make you want to change. Here's how to do it.

To begin, sit down with a piece of blank white paper. Draw an archery target—at least four rings and a bull's-eye. Ask yourself one question: Why do I want to change my body? On a second piece of paper, write down the first three answers that come to mind.

Chances are, the answers represent your Global Motivations: I want to change because I want to be healthier. I want to change because I'll die if I don't. Distill your answers into simple phrases and write them in the outermost ring.

Now go deeper. Ask again: Why do I want to change? Look for answers that stop you in your tracks. They might be serious or humorous. Write the first three you think of and turn each into a key phrase. Combine these three phrases to make one "I want . . ." sentence, and write it in the second ring.

This is a Target Motivation, and now you need to anchor it with a Motivational Mantra that will conjure up its power when you need it most. It should be simple, contain a powerful visual image if

b. A learning experience. Some things worked and others didn't.

c. A success—at least for a while—so you'll give it another try.

Studies show that most people who lose weight and successfully keep it off are hardly diet novices—they've lost the same 10, 20, or more pounds many times before. What finally turned things around? They learned from their mistakes. "You need to look at past attempts as a learning experience, not a failure," says Timothy Lohman, PhD, a professor of physiology and director of the Center for Physical Activity and Nutrition at the University of Arizona. "Say to yourself, possible, and smack you in the head like an invisible two-by-four, knocking you out of your "I gotta eat" trance. It should also contain the phrases "run from" and "run to." Here's an example of how you might come up with a Mantra:

Say your Target Motivation is to be happy, fit, and free, living life to the fullest. But right now, there's a package of Oreos screaming at you. So what's the conse-quence of giving in? How about this: You're standing in the hot summer sun, dressed in dark, shapeless clothing that feels like a shroud. You're sweating as you watch others jog by in shorts, bike down a hill in colorful clothes, and enjoy life. So "sweaty shroud" is what you run from. What do you want to run to? After some thought, you might conjure up a vision of yourself on a bike, clad in a pair of clingy biking shorts, riding up a long hill on a country road. You look and feel fit and free. You're joyful, happy, loving life. Okay. You've got it.

Motivation Mantra: "Run from sweaty shroud; run to bike ride on country road, feeling joyful and free."

Repeat this process for each of the inner rings. You'll end up with at least three Target Motivations and three Motivation Mantras, any one of which can function as your bull's-eye.

I've done this three or four times—what's the pattern here? If you can see it, then you don't have to repeat it."

If a particular weight-loss approach doesn't work for you, there's nothing wrong with starting from scratch. However, think about why the last strategy didn't work and let that guide you. As for the diet that only worked for a while, it probably won't work again because it clearly wasn't one you could stick with over the long haul.

If you answered "a," give yourself 2 points; "b," 3 points; "c," 1 point.

2. You want to lose weight to improve your health, but if you're really honest

of your life often does. That's what Diane Berry, PhD, a researcher at the Yale University School of Nursing, found in a small but telling study. Dr. Berry interviewed 20 women, ages 33 to 82, who had lost an average of 52 pounds and kept it off for seven years (two participants who were unable to maintain weight loss were also included in the study). Dr. Berry found that the positive feeling of regaining control of their lives through exercise and learning new skills such as portion control gave the successful women a sense of empowerment that helped them stay the course to long-term weight loss.

That doesn't mean that you should never try to lose weight to look great for a high school reunion, says Dr. Lohman. Meeting a short-term goal often can give you the incentive you need to keep going.

If you answered "a," give yourself 3 points; "b," 2 points; "c," 1 point.

with yourself, your main reason is that:

a. You feel like your life is out of control because you're doing things (like eating badly and sitting on the sofa way too much) that you don't want to be doing.

b. You have a wedding, high school reunion, or other big event coming up and want to look great.

c. Someone—your spouse, your mother, or an acquaintance—made a remark about your weight and you feel mortally embarrassed.

Trying to lose weight to gain someone else's approval rarely leads to success. But doing it because you want to feel in control

3. Before you start your diet, you plan to:

a. Keep doing what you've been doing—eating too much and exercising too little.

b. Get rid of the junk food in your cupboards and refrigerator.

c. Have one last blowout with all of your favorite foods.

Cleaning out your kitchen does reduce temptation. But the chips in your cupboard and the Häagen-Dazs in your freezer aren't the only things that can trip you up. A much better way to prepare is to go about life as usual and document it for a week or so by keeping a food diary: Chart the events and emotions that lead you to eat, and log your workouts—even wear a pedometer to see how much incidental activity you get each day. You'll learn what triggers you to overeat and the shortcuts you're taking to cheat yourself on physical activity. Once you do that, have one last blowout if you must. Just don't fool yourself into thinking that treating yourself to a gastronomic swan song is all you need to do to prepare.

If you answered "a," give yourself 3 points; "b," 2 points; "c," 1 point.

4. **Your boiled-down version of what it takes to lose weight is:**

   a. Eat a lot less and exercise a lot more.

   b. Cut out sweets, exercise an hour a day, and stick to steamed vegetables and lean proteins for dinner and salads for lunch.

   c. Change how you think about yourself.

Most people will need to eat less and exercise more. But it's more important to be willing to change the behaviors and thought patterns that set you up for failure. If you think you're going to fail then you will be more likely to do so—it's a self-fulfilling prophecy. "You need to say, 'That's not me' and consistently practice that," says Dr. Lohman. For instance, tell yourself, "I'm the kind of person who can turn down food in social situations and who enjoys the feeling I get from exercising."

Though many stock weight-loss rules have merit, you'll be breaking them left and right unless they work in the context of your life. "You might start out by saying, 'I'm going to go to the gym six times a week,' when the reality of your lifestyle makes that impossible," says Martin Binks, PhD, director of behavioral health at the Duke Diet & Fitness Center. It's important to be flexible, so hit the gym three times a week and walk with friends the other three days, for example, if you want to make the new you the real you.

If you answered "a," give yourself 2 points; "b," 1 point; "c," 3 points.

5. **Sometimes you just can't help yourself and you binge on a box of cookies or a pint of ice cream. The reason?**

   a. Certain emotions or events in your life trigger your binges.

   b. You love sweets and have no willpower.

   c. You don't know.

"When you're angry, what else could you do besides eat?" asks Dr. Lohman. "Or when you're bored, fearful, or tense? It's a good idea to make a list of options. It could be journaling, calling a friend, reading a book, taking a walk, pounding a pillow, or nurturing yourself in other, nonfood ways."

If you don't know why you binge, follow the advice after item 3 about keeping a food journal to help you figure it out.

If you answered "a," give yourself 3 points; "b," 1 point; "c," 2 points.

6. **You'll overcome the time barriers to exercise by:**

   a. Not even trying. There is simply no wiggle room in your schedule, so you'll just focus on your diet.

b. Breaking up workouts into short segments throughout the day.

c. Carving out a half hour to an hour a day for yourself without fail.

Figure out how to fit exercise into your day. Your success may depend on it. In an 18-month University of Pittsburgh study that tracked 104 women, ages 25 to 45, Dr. Jakicic found that those who combined diet with physical activity lost more weight than the women who tried to drop pounds using either alone. What's more, exercising seemed to help the women in the study stick to their diets—as their activity level went up, their calorie intake went down.

Does it matter if you break it up or do it in one shot? That depends on you. Another study by Dr. Jakicic found that 20 to 40 minutes of exercise daily in 10-minute bouts, five days a week, helped some women become more steadfast exercisers (while experiencing the same calorie-burning and cardiovascular-improving benefits they would if they did longer workouts). But even Dr. Jakicic admits that method isn't for everybody: "For some people, finding three or four 10-minute bouts of time is more of a hassle than finding 30 to 60 minutes." Determine what works best with your schedule.

If you answered "a," give yourself 1 point; "b," 2 points, "c," 3 points.

7. Restaurant food can make or break a diet, so:

a. You'll only go to places that have low-calorie choices.

b. You'll go to your favorite restaurants, but order more healthfully-dressing on the side, fish that's broiled instead of fried, and so on.

c. You'll eat out less often.

Limiting your dining out to restaurants that serve low-calorie meals or ordering food "your way" can be risky. "There are so many hidden calories in restaurant food," notes Dr. Jakicic. Veggies are usually tossed with butter (50 calories in ½ tablespoon); tomato sauces can be loaded with olive oil (120 calories in 1 tablespoon); and grilled fish may be brushed with fat before cooking. "And when you go to a restaurant, you may be tempted with 'Just try a bite' or 'What about some wine or dessert?'" he adds.

In his research, Dr. Jakicic has found that the more people eat out during the week, the harder it is for them to shed pounds. Your best strategy: Limit restaurant meals to no more than once a week.

If you answered "a," give yourself 2 points; "b," 1 point; "c," 3 points.

8. Your significant other:

a. Doesn't involve himself much in the things that you do.

b. Sticks his nose in everything you do.

c. Is easy to talk to and respects your wishes and decisions.

In 2001, Richard Stuart, DSW, a professor emeritus in the department of psychology at the University of Washington and a former Weight Watchers advisor, surveyed 25,000 married women to see how their relationships influenced their attempts to lose weight. To no one's surprise, Dr. Stuart found that half the women failed when their spouses weren't supportive. Less expected was his finding that many women did succeed when their spouses stayed completely out of it. The divide was about fifty-fifty. "It just shows that there is no 'correct' way," says Dr. Stuart. "Each couple has to negotiate their own terms." If you need the support of your spouse or kids, ask for it, and be explicit. "Tell them exactly what they can do to help you succeed," says Dr. Lohman.

If you answered "a" or "b," give yourself 2 points; "c," 3 points.

9. Everyone knows that the average woman shouldn't try to whittle her body down to the size of a genetically gifted supermodel. The weight that will make you happy is:

a. The same weight you were back in high school.

b. The weight that lowers all the predictors of disease—such as cholesterol and blood pressure—to a healthy level.

c. Okay, not supermodel skinny, but low enough to be considered very thin.

This is a trick question because all the answers could be right. Common wisdom is that "dreaming big" about getting small leads to failure; in fact, some research shows that women who have modest goals end up taking off more pounds than women with loftier expectations. But a recent study found a link between having "dream" weight-loss goals and successfully shedding pounds. Researchers at the University of Minnesota School of Public Health found that women with an unrealistic goal—to lose 30 percent of their body weight—lost significantly more weight after 18 months than women with less lofty goals. Though they didn't actually hit their dream weight, they felt inspired to keep going because they were confident they could stick to an eating plan and had relatively high self-esteem—all predictors of weight-loss success.

While there may be no "correct" goal for everyone, there are correct attitudes, says Jennifer Linde, PhD, lead author of the study. "It's okay to believe that you can lose a lot of weight as long as you're prepared to put in the time and effort it takes to change what you eat and get enough exercise each day."

Give yourself 3 points for answering "a," "b," or "c."

10. Your boss just threw an extra project into your lap, or your kids all have big games coming up—in other words, a wrench has been thrown into your workout schedule. You:

a. Give up on it. You'll start again when everything calms down.

b. Get up at the crack of dawn so you can get your workout in.

c. Just do more "incidental" activity, such as taking the stairs and parking farther from your destination.

It might be easier to lose weight if your life were regimented, but let's face it: Stuff happens. "That's why it's so important to have a contingency plan in place for those tough weeks," says Dr. Binks. Instead of giving up until the problem passes, try to figure out a way to continue. For example, you could go to bed an hour earlier in order

to get up earlier for your morning walk. If that doesn't work, set a reduced goal (such as getting more incidental exercise). But don't get too comfortable with a trimmed-back workout. It's just a temporary solution. Get back to your original activity goal ASAP.

If you answered "a," give yourself 1 point; "b," 3 points; "c," 2 points.

Your Score

30 TO 26 POINTS

Ready, set, go! You're prepared to change not just how much you eat and exercise, but also your daily patterns. Most important, you know how to fit these changes into your life. You've taken into consideration your job, your family, and your other commitments—

as well as the ups and downs of life—and have made a workable plan to achieve your goals. Keep in mind that you don't have to change everything at once. "Look for things that are the easiest for you to change and that will give you the most benefit; then add in other changes as you go," advises Dr. Binks.

25 TO 20 POINTS

Although you're willing to take on many of the challenges of weight loss, you're not all the way there. To better prepare, develop some strategies to deal with the inevitable hurdles. How can you find time to exercise when, for instance, your schedule changes because your kids are out of school or it's too dark to walk at night? What can you use instead of food to deal with stress or

disappointments? How can you avoid overindulging in your favorite foods? Have some support in place before you get started, whether it's friends, family, or an organized support group. "This is especially important for physical activity," says Dr. Lohman. "If you have someone to meet and hike or walk with, it can make a big difference."

BELOW 20 POINTS

You know what it takes to lose weight, but not to keep the weight off. You need to start planning—what you're going to be eating, when you're going to be exercising, who you're going to turn to for help when your resolve is low. To help you set an agenda, revisit other times you've tried to lose weight (or if it's your first time, look critically at your life to see why you're overweight in the first place). Look at the barriers you've faced and how you responded to them.

How did you handle family meals? Were you able to eat lightly or did the pressure from your family make you pile your plate too high? Why did you stop going to the gym even after paying for a membership? Did you hate the place or the exercise you were doing? Was it too hard to get there on time for classes? In the long run, losing weight—and keeping it off—is about creating a lifestyle you can maintain for the rest of your life.

If you aren't sure what's tripping you up, consider talking to a professional, such as a psychologist or nutritionist, or, if your downfall is exercise related, a fitness trainer. Once you know the obstacles you're likely to face, you can develop a game plan for success. Losing weight is never easy, but you can help yourself succeed at it if you do some of the work ahead of time.

The Real Deal

You're good to go—on the last weight-loss diet of your life. Now the real fun (yes, fun!) begins—picking a weight-loss plan that suits you best. When it comes to dieting, finding a program you can stick with is a better predictor of success than the components of the diet you choose, say researchers at Tufts University. They assigned 160 people to these diets: Ornish, Atkins, Zone, and Weight Watchers. Dropout rates after one year were 50 percent, 48 percent, 35 percent, and 35 percent, respectively. But adherence paid off, regardless of the plan. Twenty-five percent of the subjects lost 5 percent of their body weight, and 10 percent lost more than 10 percent of their body weight by year's end.

Be Fickle

Just as the first dress you try on for the upcoming high-school reunion may be all wrong for you, the first diet you try may just be a bad fit. Try another. "Mainstream diets may be interchangeable," says Michael L. Dansinger, MD, lead researcher of a study comparing diets at Tufts–New England Medical Center in Boston.

If you get tired of one, you can switch to another. You haven't failed, you just need something different. "You might be attracted to a diet in one way but annoyed in another. There may be physical chemistry but not that emotional bond or vice versa. You need something that works and that you enjoy," says Dr. Dansinger. But be patient. "If you're not enjoying your new eating plan during the first month, but you're losing weight and feeling well, stick with it another month," he says. "Many people in our study found it took two months before their taste buds changed and they learned how to enjoy their new diet."

Eventually doctors may be able to determine your "diet type" and match you with the right plan. "We're finding that gender, age, family situation, even ethnic background makes a difference," Dr. Dansinger says. "Someday you won't be alone in finding the right way to lose weight."

Until that day, read on for exciting ideas to help create a new you in the real world right now!

Keep It Real

Welcome to the real world! You've made up your mind to take off those pounds. You've picked a diet program that you feel is right for your needs. Now all you need to do is summon the heroic willpower that you'll need to succeed, right? Not so fast, Superwoman!

Maybe in the hypothetical pages of the latest diet tome, willpower always triumphs to zap fat—but you don't live in the pages of a book. You live in the real world with real-world challenges. Perhaps your family is hooked on fast food? Or your office break room looks like the snack foods aisle at the convenience store? Maybe you're working, going to school, and managing a household? How are you supposed to make time to eat right, let alone cook healthy meals?

When it comes to weight loss, you need more than willpower, says weight-loss consultant Susan Head, PhD, of Durham, North Carolina, you need *skillpower*—the ability to solve problems and strategize when things get tough and willpower fades. Willpower is like a car's engine; it gets you revved up to go. But skillpower is the steering wheel that helps you navigate obstacles.

In the beginning, willpower is strong and intoxicating. You think you'll do everything perfectly—no more sweets, an hour-long workout every day, skimpy portions—and by summer you'll look like Heather Locklear in a bikini. Skillpower says forget the bikini—focus on fitting into last year's shorts.

Rewarding yourself for achieving small goals like this keeps skillpower sharp and motivation high.

Market*Ability*

The first arena in which to flex your newfound skillpower is the supermarket. Shopping for food is an eternal tug-of-war between intention (Don't forget the asparagus) and temptation (Hey, look, Sludgy-Fudgy cookies are on sale!). Of course, temptation too often wins. And if you need evidence of its power, know that a recent *Prevention*/Food Marketing survey found that 58 percent of health-conscious people eat unhealthy foods on a regular basis.

Whether you use your supermarket to your healthiest advantage is up to you. Because most of us do a lot of shopping

(84 percent of consumers prepare home-cooked meals—presumably with store-bought ingredients—at least three times a week), it's important to learn to sleuth out the healthiest products while navigating the supermarket smorgasbord.

For guidance on how to be a smarter shopper, we consulted Lisa Sasson, RD, a clinical assistant professor at New York University, mother of two, and twice-a-week shopper who lives by this truism: "If you resist it at the grocery store, you only have to resist it once. If you take it home, you have to resist it every hour of every day." Here's her advice:

Come prepared. Even before you walk through the supermarket doors, start strategizing, recommends Sasson. "The first thing you're going to do is shop the perimeter," she explains. "That's where the whole-foods action is." That often means walking through a bakery filled with dangerously enticing, fresh-from-the-oven smells. Until recently, fruits and vegetables were the first thing you saw when you entered. Today, 88 percent of supermarkets have in-store bakeries, and some are near the entrance. "Smells, especially cinnamon, will get shoppers to buy baked goods," warns Kevin Kelley, founding partner of Shook Kelley, a marketing firm that consults with national grocery chains. So hold your nose if you have to.

Beware of "innocent" foods. The produce section has pyramids of gleaming fruits, big leafy greens, stacks of bright red berries, and—tucked beside the stack—cream cheese dip loaded with fat and calories. "They're trying to tempt you by offering a healthful food with an unhealthful one, as if there's innocence by association," Sasson says of the marketing strategy called *vignetting.* "There's also a caramel-apple kit next to the apples. I'm seeing this more often and I tell my clients, 'Buy the fruits and vegetables, but skip the dip and candy coating—you don't need them." Stick to your list.

Skip the free lunch. Perhaps you're heading to the deli but you're waylaid by a smiling employee handing out samples of rich, fatty-looking dips. One taste couldn't hurt, could it? Well, yes—free samples can add unwanted pounds.

"If you don't want a food in your house, don't sample it," Sasson says. Once you've tasted it, you're much more likely to buy it. (Kelley adds that most supermarkets "sample" poor-selling products as a way to get them out the door.) A similar principle applies to coupons. "Don't clip a coupon if it's not for a healthy food," says Sasson. If you can get a discount on your preferred soy milk or bagged salad mix, great. But three bags of leftover Christmas candy for the price of one is no health bargain, no matter how much money you save.

Ask for deli directions. When you're buying deli meat, choose fresh over processed versions, which are more likely to be high in salt, sugar, and preservatives. Your butcher will know the difference. As for side dishes, coleslaw made with vinegar, carrot salad, and hummus are better nutritional choices than white deli salads such as macaroni and potato salads and traditional coleslaw—all doused with lots of high-calorie, high-fat mayonnaise.

Be a cheese wiz. Most markets have two cheese sections: one with domestic cheeses such as American and sliced Pepper Jack,

DROP 800 CALORIES A DAY—EASY!

On your next shopping trip, load up on fruits and veggies and skip the candy and cookie aisles; then try eating from dessert rather than dinner plates. Those two small steps added up to a huge but painless calorie reduction in a Pennsylvania State University study of 24 women. For four weeks, the women ate similar foods one day a week. Then, on the following day, the researchers cut about 544 calories by replacing fat and sugar with fruits and vegetables. They also trimmed 256 calories by cutting portion sizes by one-quarter. Amazingly, the women didn't increase the amount of food they ate to compensate on day two, although they were allowed to eat as much as they chose.

The magic: Produce fills you up with calorie-free fiber and water, and small reductions in portion size don't register as deprivation.

and a second, usually near the deli, with a wider variety of imported and fancy cheeses. Sasson prefers the latter. The reason: "You'll find a lot of more flavorful choices—blue, Parmesan, Camembert. A little of these varieties goes a long way, so you use much less, and that means fewer calories and fat for all the flavor." Sasson learned this while doing supermarket comparisons in Europe, where many people eat cheese every day and don't get as fat as Americans do. Tiny portions of flavor-packed cheeses (which, by the way, are not diet food by any measure) may help explain that paradox.

Choose select meats. Next up is the meat section. Sasson warns not to buy the government grades of prime and choice; they indicate marbling—a polite way of saying "lots of fat." A better idea: Choose select cuts, which are the leanest, most healthful, and most affordable meats you can find.

Most meat is packaged in family-size cuts. Portion control is key to weight control, and supersized beef doesn't help. The fix: Ask the butcher to package the exact amount you need. Buying less doesn't guarantee you'll eat less, but it sure makes it easier.

Attack snacks. "Wherever there's temptation, shop like a man," Sasson recommends. Turns out, there's a big gender gap in shopping styles. Men do surgical-strike shopping. They know what they want, and they go get it. Women browse, pause, read, and choose. There are times when each strategy is more useful—and yields healthier results. But when you're in a danger zone, browsing yields to temptation.

If you do enter the snack zone, do so with

purpose. Snacks are prime temptation territory—almost 60 percent are bought on impulse. For *occasional* indulging, Sasson likes the trend of "fun size" single-serving packs of sugary treats, which are often 100 calories each. Read labels, though, and make sure it really is a single serving. A snack pack of chocolate cookies that looks like one serving might actually be a surprising four servings, each with 140 calories.

Skip the beverage aisle. Don't even go into the beverage aisle, which can leave a bad taste in your mouth. Sasson's advice is to nix all sugary drinks. "Kids grow up associating satisfying their thirst with a sweet drink, and that's one of the culprits in pediatric obesity."

What's more, Sasson points out, with increasing frequency those high-calorie drinks aren't limited to the beverage aisle. More than 10 percent of the calories we consume come from soft drinks and juice, and food companies are making it easier to guzzle calories. Sugary yogurt drinks are shelved with the plain yogurt, high-calorie smoothies in with the juices, sugar-packed iced teas alongside the unsweetened ones, flavored, sweetened milks in with the dairy, and sugary coffee drinks in with the coffee. There are even sodas in coolers by the checkout to tempt you as you're leaving.

Look high and low for healthy foods. You might have to bring along your binoculars to spot the reduced-sugar or no-sugar-added cereals, such as Grape-Nuts, which are usually relegated to the nosebleed shelves.

Sasson explains that high-sugar, practically fiber-free cereals are lined up at waist level, which corresponds to where the average kid's line of vision is centered.

In any store, some products are right in your face and others are harder to find. Many of those easy-to-spot products are paying to be there. Twelve percent of supermarket profits come from so-called placement fees, money that manufacturers pay grocers for premium shelf space.

Ditch "diet" foods. If you're on a diet, the last place you should shop is the diet foods aisle. "Don't bother buying something like energy bars unless you're a marathon runner or you want to gain weight. Most of that stuff is low-carb, not low-calorie," Sasson explains, and they can undermine your diet. "Studies show that you might even be in danger of overeating and packing on pounds because of what they call the *SnackWell's phenomenon*—you eat more because you think it's healthy."

Shop like a woman. Always head to the freezer section last so those foods spend less time melting in your cart. When you get to frozen entrées and meals, Sasson explains

that this is one area in which you should use your feminine ways. The reason? There's so much variation here. "If you're trying to find the frozen pasta dish without added sugar, the frozen pizza with the most veggies, or the entrée with the most fiber, you have to read labels carefully to make good choices." For example, Sasson warns that some companies are trying to get men to buy more frozen meals—by making the portions (and the calorie count) bigger. That's fine—unless you're a woman watching her weight.

Check yourself out. Waiting in line to pay for your purchases, you can't help but notice the racks of candy and soft drinks in your path. A whopping 20 percent of customers succumb to last-minute impulse buying, and, no surprise, there is no Brussels sprouts display here. So bury yourself in a juicy gossip magazine instead. Or try a new alternative: the self-checkout station, where only 12 percent of customers make those last-minute, indulgent food buys.

Real Meals

Too many dieters believe they need to tiptoe through the kitchen as if it were a minefield but, in reality, the kitchen can be an oasis of healthy self-nurturing.

"Before you embark on your next last-chance diet, give yourself the gift of believing that you're worth it. Start eating one hot meal a day, no matter what," advises Geneen Roth, *Prevention* columnist and author of six books on emotional eating.

"Hot meals are real food. Hot meals nourish you. A Snickers bar tastes good, but after you've finished it, you don't feel as if you've eaten. So you go scrounging around for more. Soon you find yourself standing in your kitchen eating cold pizza from three days ago. Then, although it's 10:00 p.m., you notice your child's dinner leftovers, and you eat them, too. That doesn't do it either, so you hunt for more food and become less discriminating as it gets later. Two hours pass and you're eating a bowl of stale popcorn with spoonfuls of peanut butter, cold hot fudge, and slices of Cheddar cheese. Not a

winning combination, but it's late and you don't want to take the time to cook a meal. Besides, eating at night is not supposed to be good for you, so you're only going to take "one more bite."

If your life is arranged so that you don't have time to eat a hot meal every day—even if it's soup, scrambled eggs, or just a vegetable potpie heated in the microwave—Roth suggests it's time to question your priorities. Most women are busy nourishing everyone else, giving food in the form of time and attention to children and spouses and friends, and leaving the dregs for themselves. When you don't have a built-in way of giving yourself time and attention, food becomes the main source of sweetness in your life. And "treats" are usually cold. Diet sodas, cookies, chips, protein bars, and frozen yogurt are not real nourishment. Neither is coffee. And neither is anything sweet dunked in coffee.

"Show yourself that you matter, that you do not come in second, or last, or not at all. You have to decide that there's a bottom line, that you have basic needs and they are not negotiable," explains Roth. Although it's tempting to view a hot meal as a luxury, it's not. "One hot meal a day is a basic bodily necessity that also gives your subconscious the message that you've had it with leftovers and that you're worth the kindness and grace inherent in sitting down and eating a real meal. Eating one hot meal a day is a way of saying that you want the real thing: a whole life of main courses."

Sticking to a regular meal schedule has helped celebrity chef Sara Moulton keep off the 12 pounds she dropped, with the help of Weight Watchers, from her petite 5-foot frame. "When you're hungry, your resistance to snack on tempting foods plummets," says Moulton, host of *Sara's Secrets* on the Food Network, author of *Sara's Secrets for Weeknight Meals*, and executive chef at *Gourmet* magazine.

Eating on the run, while standing, or in front of the TV are big no-no's in Moulton's house. "If you're going to eat, plate your food, sit down, and commit to it," she recommends. Moulton practices what she preaches, sitting down to three meals a day and even putting her late-afternoon snack of 15 almonds in a bowl.

Fresh *and* Fast

Real meals are easy when you use skillpower in the kitchen. It's possible to make delicious dinners on even your busiest days—and we're not talking takeout. If you've followed the supermarket shopping guidelines in the preceding section, you're more than halfway to your healthy eating goals. The trick is choosing uncomplicated recipes (like the ones in *Eat Up Slim Down*) that are well suited to midweek meals, and then employing some clever tips for keeping prep and cooking time to a minimum.

FAMILY MATTERS

Setting family goals for healthier eating may help all of you stay out of the plus-size department, indicates an Arizona State University study of 6,400 teens. Those in families with healthy habits—like eating breakfast every morning—were 33 percent less likely to be overweight. We asked Samuel Gladding, PhD, a family counseling professor at Wake Forest University, for some tips on teamwork.

- Have a family meeting to take stock of how meals could be improved for the whole family.

- Ask a family member who is reluctant to participate to try the family's diet changes for a few weeks—and then decide whether to continue.

- Encourage flexibility. If someone refuses to join in, ask him or her to cook something else to eat with the family.

- Increase cooperation by cutting back rather than eliminating favorite foods. For example, smaller dessert portions can lead to substantial weight loss.

- Let each person pick his or her own rewards for healthy eating. They needn't be family based—like a night at the movies or a sports outing.

The convenience revolution in "real" foods, particularly produce, has made eating to lose weight easier than ever before. The old too-busy-to-cook excuse falls flat on its face with the availability of washed and ready-to-eat fresh vegetables like spinach, baby carrots, sugar snap peas, broccoli florets, cauliflower florets, and mixed salad greens. Even nutrition superstar kale comes bagged and chopped, ready to stir-fry in minutes.

Another often overlooked shortcut: using frozen foods, especially produce, which FDA research has shown to be just as nutritious as fresh. That's not all: Frozen vegetables—which require no cutting, shucking, slicing, or dicing—aren't just big time-savers. Because there's no waste from trimming or chopping, they're also economical. Clean-up time is pared down, too.

We turned to fast and healthy cooking expert Marie Simmons, author of *Fresh & Fast* and *Fig Heaven*, for some other time-saving tips:

- Purchase precut meats or choose cuts of meat and poultry—such as flank steak, boneless pork loin chops, boneless chicken and turkey breasts, and ground sirloin—that cook quickly. Most seafood can also be prepared in a snap.

- Keep a stash of convenient staples on hand. Musts for a well-stocked pantry include dried pasta, instant brown rice, reduced-sodium chicken broth, chopped dry-packed sun-dried tomatoes, dried onions, and olive oil.

- Multitask by boiling pasta and vegetables together in the same pot, adding the veggies later so that they're cooked through at the same time.

- Opt for precooked, canned beans. They require no prep time and are just as nutritious and flavorful as dry beans that must be soaked and cooked. Rinse and drain before adding to your recipe.

- Shorten prep time by buying jarred minced garlic in oil, grated cheese, prechopped dry-packed sun-dried tomatoes, and frozen or fresh chopped onions. Using ready-to-go ingredients shaves off the prep time.

- Choose the right size pots and pans—it will help liquids boil faster and allow heat to penetrate more evenly into food, thus speeding cooking.

- Stock unsweetened loose-pack frozen strawberries, raspberries, blueberries, and sliced peaches for quick desserts. In the pantry, keep cans of packed-in-their-own-juices peaches, pineapple, and other fruits.

Lunch Lessons

The average "lunch hour" has shrunk to 36 minutes. So tapping into your skillpower for the midday meal is more important than ever.

Have you ever noticed how soon you feel hungry again after eating a typical fast-food meal? That's because there's so little fiber in it to keep you satisfied. Given the salt, sugar, and saturated and trans fats that fast food is loaded with, "You're basically putting greasy sawdust in your gas tank," according to *Prevention* advisor Elizabeth Somer.

And don't get us started on the calories in most drive-thru meals: A Burger King Double Hamburger packs 410 calories, and while six McDonald's Chicken McNuggets weigh in at 250 calories, that's for a little more than 3 ounces, which isn't likely to keep you filled up for long. Meals like these put you on a fast track to being overweight, and all the health problems that tag along with it.

"Thinking about lunch even a half hour earlier would allow you to make sounder, less emotional choices," says Cindy Moore, RD, director of nutrition therapy at the Cleveland Clinic and a spokesperson for the American Dietetic Association. Use your newfound skillpower to anticipate and avoid "must eat now" situations. "We're so busy that if we wait to listen to our bodies, it's often too late."

Baltimore nutritionist Colleen Pierre, RD, recommends cutting back on fast-food lunches to once or twice a week—and making better choices. At Taco Bell, for instance, the Bean Burrito has about half the calories and one-third the saturated fat of the Zesty Chicken Border Bowl with dressing. On the remaining days, try the soup and salad bar at a nearby supermarket or organize a weekly potluck lunch and limit desserts to fruit.

Pack Some Power

To really save time and be in control of your own (and your family's) lunch food choices, consider packing your own meals. "Packing a nutritious lunch takes some thought, but it doesn't have to take all night," says Sara Moulton, Food Network celebrity chef. Her fast-packing strategy is to set aside an hour on Sundays and prepare several lunches at once. You can brown-bag the finished meals and store them on a large tray or baking sheet in the fridge for easy grab-and-go in the morning. Here are two easy ideas.

Nacho kit. Pack ingredients in small containers (and include a plastic spoon): 1 cup baked corn chips (look for no trans fats), ½ cup fat-free refried black beans, ¼ cup shredded chicken, 2 tablespoons shredded low-fat Cheddar cheese, ½ cup mixed shredded lettuce and grated carrots, and 2 tablespoons mild salsa. Sides: 1 cup red grapes and 1 bottle of water or 1 cup fat-free milk. Other time-savers: Buy rotisserie chicken, bagged grated carrots, and shredded cheese.

Turkey "sushi." Mix ¼ cup cooked whole wheat couscous with 1 teaspoon reduced-fat mayo to bind the grains together. Spread on two slices of low-fat turkey lunchmeat. Lay grated carrots, sliced celery, and sliced red bell pepper between them. Roll up and cut crosswise into 1" pieces. Sides: 1 string cheese, 1 bottle of water or 1 cup fat-free milk, and pineapple chunks.

Turn to page 78 for more portable meals.

Office Acumen

On-the-job training is the true test for your burgeoning skillpower. Recent studies, including two from the American Dietetic Association, show that 9 in 10 of us snack on the job. Corporate America seems to be turning into a giant convenience store, where eating on the job has become a necessity for the time-crunched and stressed. Perhaps it's the doughnuts that the supervisor brought in for a job well done? Candy from the vending machine? Microwave popcorn in the cafeteria? Chips in the bottom desk drawer?

"Most office food isn't satisfying," says nutritionist Colleen Pierre. "Doughnuts, coffee, pastries, and candy give you temporary energy, but you're hungry a few hours later." It doesn't take long for the quick fix to become a pattern.

Pierre stresses the importance of improving overall eating habits, not just office behavior. Real balanced meals for breakfast, lunch, and dinner will train your appetite for healthier snacking. For break-

NUMBERS GAME

How's this for a simple diet plan: Stick to foods that fill you up but have the fewest calories, and you'll lose weight. That's the theory behind *The Volumetrics Eating Plan* by Barbara Rolls, PhD, RD, a professor of nutrition at Pennsylvania State University. She developed a formula to help you quickly spot the least calorie-dense foods: Divide the number of calories per serving by the serving weight in grams. Choose foods that score less than 1 most of the time, choose those that score 1 to 2 occasionally, and minimize those that score 2 or more. Use Dr. Rolls's formula to choose packaged foods on the fly, but start with these general food categories.

- Anytime (calorie density of less than 1): fruits, vegetables, low-fat dairy foods
- Sometimes (calorie density of 1 to 2): pasta, fish, chicken, beans, bread, cereal
- Rarely (calorie density of greater than 2): french fries, pretzels, beef, ice cream

fast, try a frozen whole grain waffle, toasted and topped with yogurt and fruit or a high-fiber cereal or unsweetened instant oatmeal.

At lunchtime, focus on eating. Instead of

RAISING THE BAR

Energy bars were invented to prevent athletes from "bonking"—running out of steam in the middle of a marathon or a hike up Kilimanjaro. But most of us grab them for a convenient, neat-to-eat mid-afternoon snack in front of our computers, where we exercise little but our fingers. These high-carb energy boosters can deliver instant zip: Carbohydrates are the fuel of choice for human cells everywhere, including the brain.

However, dietitians tend to pooh-pooh energy bars because many are nothing more than candy in health clothing. A single bar can contain up to 22 grams of sugar, but that's the carbohydrates these bars use for rocket fuel. With the help of *Prevention* advisor Elizabeth Somer, we learned what to look for to raise the bar on these snacks' nutritional profiles: Choose a bar that is relatively low in calories (less than 250) and contains at least 8 grams of protein, the essential ingredient in a pick-me-up snack. When protein and carbs team up, you get staying power. You also need 3 to 5 grams of fiber, and no more than 2 grams of saturated fat in a single bar.

A warning: Energy bars are so handy, you can chomp your way through an entire box in no time. It's easy to tell if you've developed a nasty energy-bar habit: If your car or gym bag is overflowing with wrappers, you're flagged, Lady.

multitasking, give yourself 15 to 20 minutes to concentrate on your meal. You'll feel more relaxed and satisfied, and therefore less tempted later by peanut M&Ms, says Pierre.

For an afternoon snack, Pierre suggests that peanut butter is one of the best foods to keep in your desk. Spread some on a banana, apple, celery, carrots, or whole grain crackers. Pick up ready-to-eat baby carrots or apple slices (sold in a bag of five small packages) and prewashed and precut celery sticks. In addition, keep fresh fruit in the office fridge and stock your desk with raisins or dried cranberries, trail mix (without the chocolate bits), and single-serve applesauce and fruit cups, which stay fresh until opened.

Keep It Revved Up

Moving your body every day, whether climbing the stairs at work or practicing Pilates at the health center, can be a potent partner in shedding pounds.

Exercise is a no-brainer strategy for losing and maintaining weight, and for cutting your heart disease risk, according to psychologist Thomas A. Wadden, PhD, director of the Weight and Eating Disorders Program at the University of Pennsylvania. The proof? Among the many studies showing a direct link between a lower body mass index (BMI) and more time spent exercising, University of Pittsburgh researchers found recently that dieting women who exercised five days a week for 50 to 60 minutes each time lost 15 percent of

their body weight—a whopping 23 pounds, on average—in just six months. Those who kept it up maintained their new trimmer silhouettes for the next six months.

But the biggest reason to exercise is the health benefits, Dr. Wadden says. "Researchers at the Cooper Institute have found that it reduces heart attack risk even if you're overweight. And as you get older, strength training will help prevent the natural loss of muscle density and the drop in metabolic rate."

If you're the type who's allergic to exercise (or think you are) and you believe you can shed those pounds simply by eating less, think again. Dieting alone—and not exercising—can cause the loss of valuable

OM-AZING! YOGA CURBS WEIGHT GAIN

New research suggests that yoga may help stave off middle-age spread. A survey that tracked weight gain in 15,500 adults from age 45 to 55 revealed that the normal-weight people who practiced yoga at least 30 minutes a week for four of those years gained 3 fewer pounds (9.5 versus 12.6) than those who didn't. Even better, overweight yogis lost 5 pounds over the decade, while their non-yoga-practicing peers gained an additional 14.

"Yoga may not be a big calorie burner, but it helps you become more aware of your body, so you're more sensitive to feeling full from overeating," says lead researcher and yoga practitioner Alan R. Kristal, DrPH, of the Fred Hutchinson Cancer Research Center in Seattle. "Yoga also relieves stress, so you may be less likely to mindlessly stuff yourself." You can find affordable yoga classes at many Ys and community centers.

muscle. In a small study at Vanderbilt University, women who cut calories without exercising lost lean mass and *decreased* their daily metabolism by 100 calories after only two weeks.

To put the brakes on the muscle-for-fat swap, pick up some dumbbells at least twice a week. Resistance training has been shown to preserve—and even replenish—muscle, and it helps fight fat. If weights aren't your cup of tea, try Pilates, swimming, or power yoga—all of which will give you toned, firm, and shapely muscles. For best results, you may want to consult a fitness trainer who can identify your specific body needs (see "The Shape You're In," page 26).

Gym Gems

To increase the chances of success in your fitness program, consider joining a gym. Recently, scientists at the University of Western Australia studied 126 women and found that those who exercised at a gym were four times more likely to stick with their routine than were those who worked out at home. Although the women in the study were supervised while they exercised, you don't need a trainer by your side to get better results at a health club than at home, says Wayne Westcott, PhD, who has observed thousands of women's workout habits as research director for the South Shore YMCA in Quincy, Massachusetts. "Gyms offer a range of activities to keep you from getting bored," he says. "And you typically work out harder in a gym because you're less likely to get distracted by the phone, kids, or laundry."

Plus, it's easier than ever to get what you

need. Health clubs are catering to women more than ever before—offering saunas, stairclimbers, even child care, and other female-friendly features. The result: more personal attention and convenience, and an emphasis on machines that trim and tone. Class schedules once dominated by standard-issue aerobic sessions now have jazzy new lineups including Cardio Salsa, Urban Yoga, and Pilates Strength. Plus, not a gym in the country can get away with omitting personal services such as customized fitness training and counseling in nutrition and weight loss.

If you're still finding excuses not to exercise, consult these motivational messages from our experts:

Excuse: "I have no time."
Solution: Streamline your workout.

Look for a gym—ideally one within 15 minutes of your home or office—that has circuit training. These quick workouts mix short bouts of cardio with resistance training for a total-body workout of less than an hour.

Excuse: "I'm strapped for cash."
Solution: Look for the basics.

You don't need a juice bar and Aveda gel in the locker room to get a great workout. Small, independent gyms may have fewer extras and luxuries, but they make up for it in price and service. Typically, small facilities charge $20 to $40 a month, depending on the region—often less than half of what you'd pay at a larger club. Curves gyms are also pared down (no pools, locker rooms, or classes), but at only $29 a month, their circuit training is a great bargain.

If you want a full-service facility, check out the local YMCA. Most have a weight room, pools, classes, racquetball, a running track, and more. Other low-cost or possibly free options include church gyms (free), municipally run gyms (as little as $75 a year), and university gyms (often free or nearly free to neighbors).

Excuse: "I'm stuck at home with the kids."
Solution: Put the kids in gym class.

The International Health, Racquet & Sportsclub Association (IHRSA) reports that 70 percent of clubs offer child care and more are adding it each year. Gyms generally charge $1 to $5 an hour per child, but many places will include several free hours each week with your membership.

To make sure you're getting quality child

THE SHAPE YOU'RE IN

In "The Year of a New You!" chapter, we learned that not all diets work equally well for all dieters. Not all exercise routines work well for all dieters either. "By building a body-sculpting plan targeted to *your* figure, you can exercise smarter—not harder—and get results fast," says Chris Freytag, one of the nation's top fitness trainers. Before planning any exercise program, determine what shape your body is in to maximize the results.

Body Type: Overweight (need to lose 20+ pounds)

Many women in this category try to starve themselves thin, and they inevitably regain the weight. "It's really hard to lose weight and keep it off with diet alone," says Freytag. "Along with healthy eating, women need consistent aerobic activity to shed fat for once and for all. When you move your body, you burn calories. That's what really keeps weight off."

Body Type: Soccer Mom Spread

Once you hit your late 30s, it's harder to lose or even maintain your weight. Life gets in the way—job, kids, and aging parents all conspire to steal exercise time. Making matters worse, you start losing muscle tissue, so your metabolism slows. The result: an extra 10 to 15 pounds that seem impossible to shake. "To drop those stubborn pounds, you need high-intensity cardio and full-body strength training," says Freytag.

Body Type: Normal Weight, But Flabby

It can happen to anyone: After years of getting by on "good genes" or following the same tried-and-true exercise routines, we start to go soft. "Women with

care—not minimally supervised chaos—pick a gym that has a full-time day care center manager, and speak to him or her before joining. Also, ask what kinds of kids' programs they offer. Many places have special kids' fitness classes and craft sessions, which are much more fun for kids (and less worrisome for moms) than unstructured playtime.

Excuse: "I find the gym totally intimidating."
Solution: Try a women-only club.

Such a gym can be a haven if you're just getting back into a routine.

Another option is a more intimate, hands-on facility. "Small gyms are often more reassuring to the mid-30s or mid-40s this body type aren't overweight, but they're overfat; they lack lean muscle tissue," explains Freytag. "They need more weight resistance to sculpt a feminine, sexy shape."

Body Type: Pear Shape

Thirty-six percent of women bemoan their hips, butt, and thighs as the places where fat takes up residence, reports a poll by the National Women's Health Resource Center. "Bottom-heavy women also tend to be narrow up top," says Freytag. "By focusing on upper-body resistance training to sculpt shapely shoulders and cardio to trim their lower half, pear-shaped women can create a trimmed, better proportioned shape."

Body Type: Apple Shape (Potbelly)

Even otherwise slim women can sport a stubborn belly bulge. "When the deep transverse abdominals become stretched from pregnancy or weak from lack of use, your belly sticks out no matter what your size," says Freytag. Also, it's common to store excess fat around the middle as you get older. "To lose it, you need core work—especially Pilates-based moves—to pull in those abs and enough cardio to shed unwanted fat."

mom who has several kids, hasn't worked out in years, and doesn't want to deal with a bunch of 20-year-olds dancing around in spandex," says Todd Rotruck, a personal trainer in Greensboro, North Carolina, who has worked at several gyms in the past 12 years. "They're less of a meat market, and staff members pride themselves on learning members' first names and tend to dish out

more personal instruction and individual attention than staffers at the big clubs do."

Excuse: "I keep strange hours."
Solution: Find an all-night gym.

Health clubs are working overtime to accommodate early birds and night owls. Many large chains are open around-the-clock, such as Life Time Fitness, Crunch, and (no surprise) 24 Hour Fitness. Some small gyms are also willing to make special arrangements to fit your schedule if you ask.

Excuse: "I'm always on the road."
Solution: Get a gym passport.

Until airport gyms are commonplace—currently, only a handful of airports have them—joining a club that is a member of IHRSA's Passport program is a reasonable alternative. The program gives members of participating IHRSA clubs guest privileges (some clubs still charge a small guest fee) at more than 3,000 facilities worldwide.

Choose *Fast* Foods

To complement your accelerated exercise, you'll want to eat more fast foods. No, not fast food as in burger and fries, *fast* foods—in moderated portions—that actually increase your metabolic rate and help you lose weight faster. The following trio of easy-to-follow weight-loss guidelines comes from New York University nutritionist Lisa Young, PhD, RD, author of *The Portion Teller*. The recommendations are designed to boost your metabolism and work with your changing body so you can firm up, lose belly fat, get back into proportion, and drop weight—fast.

Fair Share

The first principle—with whatever foods fit into your diet program—is portion control, a key factor in curbing calorie intake. Two Cornell University studies on college students found that Americans tend to eat most of what we're served at a meal, regardless of how much it is. Moreover, the

LOSE WEIGHT WHILE YOU SLEEP— NO KIDDING!

Every coin has a flip side. Toss the exercise–weight loss token and what do you get? Deep, restorative sleep.

"You snooze, you lose" may be truer than anyone thought. A new Columbia University study suggests that the fewer Zs you get, the more likely you are to pack on the pounds. Researchers studied the sleeping habits of more than 18,000 people and found that those who get by on less than four hours of sleep a night are 73 percent more likely to be obese than people who slumber seven to nine hours nightly. Even those who caught six hours were 23 percent more likely to be obese. On the other hand, those who averaged 10 hours of shut-eye a night were 11 percent less likely to be obese.

"When you're deprived of sleep, the effect on your appetite hormones is not unlike undereating," says study author Steven Heymsfield, MD. "Your leptin levels fall as your ghrelin levels shoot up. This triggers hunger." These hormonal changes may also signal the body to put the brakes on metabolism and hold on to fat stores more tenaciously, he adds.

authors found that we don't compensate for our clean-plate-club habits by eating less later on. The results add to the growing evidence that overeating is often an unconscious habit.

Fats That Sizzle

The second principle is to add selected fats back into your diet. Yes, healthy fats are good for your heart and overall health. But they're critical to weight loss, too. New research from Washington University in St. Louis suggests that dietary fat triggers gene activity in the liver, which spurs metabolism. Body fat stores alone (like the jiggly stuff hanging around your thighs and belly) failed to set these activities in motion.

Yummy ways to bolster healthy fats in your diet include: drizzling (not pouring) a little extra virgin olive oil on pasta or bread; adding half a chopped avocado or a small fistful of nuts to a tossed salad; and eating olives as snacks. "You do need fat in your diet, in moderation—the healthiest are fatty acids that come from vegetables and fish," Dr. Young says.

Protein Pushes It

The third cornerstone is protein. New research from the University of Illinois at Urbana-Champaign suggests that adding more fish, poultry, and lean meat to your diet will accelerate the benefits of your workouts. In a four-month study that followed 24 women on a fitness plan, one group ate about 9 ounces of high-quality protein a day; the other ate 5 ounces of protein and twice as much carbohydrate-rich food, such as bread and rice. Both consumed the same number of calories, but

NUTS FOR YOU

When 52 overweight women and men followed a 1,000-calorie-a-day diet for 24 weeks, those who ate almonds at meals and snack time lost 18 percent of their body weight, while those whose treats were carbohydrate-based (wheat crackers, baked potato, air-popped popcorn) lost just 11 percent. The nut eaters whittled their waists by 14 percent; the carb snackers, 9 percent. Researchers from the City of Hope National Medical Center in Duarte, California, suspect that the protein, fat, and fiber in almonds keep you feeling full longer—and that not all the calories in almonds are absorbed thanks to the tough cell walls of these nuts. Walnuts, pecans, unsalted peanuts, and other nuts should have similar effects—they're packed with fiber and good fats, too. Have a handful (no more—they're also high in calories) in place of your usual midmorning or afternoon snack.

the protein group lost 21.5 percent of their body fat (compared with 15 percent for the carb group) and 47 percent more weight. The protein-rich diet boosted the benefits of the exercise plan, say researchers, because high-quality protein contains a high level of the amino acid leucine. Leucine, working together with insulin, helps stimulate protein synthesis in muscle, which revs metabolism. Eating eggs or yogurt for breakfast, nuts and cottage cheese for snacks, and lean meats with meals or snacks are all good ways to add protein.

Now the Magic Happens

You've analyzed your emotional and physical dietary needs. You've made the commitment to lose those extra pounds. You've selected the diet plan that will work best for *your* body. You've learned how to shop wisely for real foods and to prepare satisfying meals
in a snap. You've built movement into your routine. You've got this diet thing covered, right? Mmmmm, better to take it one day at a time. From the open house on New Year's Day to the black tie bash on New Year's Eve, there are 364 days stuffed with booby traps that can derail even the most dedicated dieter.

You're cruising along on your new diet when you run up against an invitation to a party, a wedding, or a business function that will surely feature irresistible puff pastry hors d'oeuvres, flowing cocktails, and a lavish dessert selection. The challenge will make bypassing the supermarket bakery look like a cakewalk. What's for certain: If you make it past this event, another will follow on its heels. National holidays, birthday parties, and scores of other impromptu celebrations—a promotion, a good report card, even making a deadline—will come this year and all the years that follow.

"Because we don't have established patterns of eating in these circumstances, every occasion offers different temptations," says Brian Wansink, PhD, a Cornell University food psychologist who has studied guests' eating patterns at Super Bowl parties, office celebrations, and other types of get-togethers. "You need to go into the event with a strategy."

And what might that be? We called upon leading experts for advice on how to handle diet-busting situations that crop up throughout the year. Just jump into the calendar on *your* starting month and then double back to January to benefit fully and let your *New You* emerge!

January

New Year's Brunch

Enjoy a toasted whole grain waffle with berries and low-fat yogurt immediately after you wake up. "The slightest bit of hunger will wear away your ability to stick to your resolution," says Arthur S. Agatston, MD, author of *The South Beach Diet*. Why waffles? If you have them for breakfast, you'll be less tempted by the ones dripping with butter and syrup at brunch.

Friday Night

In our living-for-the-weekend-society, Friday night might as well be a holiday. That's why it's important not to weigh yourself on this Friday—OR ANY OTHER. If you like what you see on the scale Friday morning, you might be tempted to splurge on Friday or Saturday night. A better time for a weigh-in: Monday morning, when you'll see the results of your weekend behavior.

February

Groundhog Day

If that prognosticating rodent predicts six more weeks of winter, your already winter-comprised levels of serotonin—a feel-good brain chemical that acts as a brake on hunger—may plummet even lower. Instead of burrowing in your bed with an entire carryout supreme pizza, rent the classic Bill Murray romantic comedy *Groundhog Day*. Laughter can improve bloodflow and contribute to a healthier heart, according to a study conducted at the University of Maryland Medical Center. Then make your own healthy pizza with a ready-made 100 percent whole wheat thin crust, ¾ cup of your favorite tomato sauce, ¾ cup shredded reduced-fat mozzarella cheese, and ½ cup of sliced mushrooms. Eat one-third of the pie, which is a larger portion than two Pizza Hut slices and will save you 137 calories.

Super Bowl Sunday

Develop a game plan for this day, which ranks first in snack foods consumed. On offense, bring a bowl of air-popped popcorn sprinkled with a little Parmesan cheese; it'll satisfy your craving for a crunchy and salty snack—and 4 cups have the same number of calories that just 14 potato chips have. On defense, don't eat anything—even finger foods—without putting it on a plate, and sit where you have to walk in front of the TV to get food. Imagine the embarrassment of blocking your friends' views of the big play.

Valentine's Day

Ask for dark chocolate–dipped strawberries: They're festive, tasty, filled with antioxidants, and 40 calories apiece. If you absolutely must have the box of chocolates, instead of hinting for chocolate truffles (70 calories each), slip your honey a note requesting low-calorie truffles (at around 30 calories each) made without artificial sweeteners.

March

Academy Awards Night

If your goal is to be as svelte as the glamorous movie stars parading down the red carpet, use the trick that New York City weight-loss psychologist Stephen Gullo, PhD, gives his celebrity clients: Suck on a menthol-flavored lozenge instead of grazing on hors d'oeuvres. It'll keep your mouth busy for up to a half hour for a mere 15 calories. And the weight-loss Oscar goes to . . . YOU!

St. Patrick's Day

Trade one green beer (8 ounces of light beer has about 70 calories) for an iced green tea. Not only is green tea virtually calorie

free, but preliminary research suggests that it's a metabolism-booster, too.

April

Easter

Lay off the chocolate eggs in favor of a beautifully decorated hard-boiled egg. One is just 78 calories—a nutritious snack anytime—and it's a terrific source of choline, an important brain chemical.

Tax Day

Breathe deeply between bites and when you do nibble, pay attention to the food's taste and feel. Otherwise, in your frenzied state, you'll mindlessly shovel in food, says Ann Pardo, director of behavioral health services at Canyon Ranch Health Resort in Tucson.

Earth Day

Honoring our mother planet can be a reminder to heed our mothers' dictum: Eat your vegetables (shoot for 9 daily servings). Women who eat little or no meat are less likely to be overweight than omnivores, new Tufts University research found. The study of 55,500 women revealed that those who were

diverted as you focus on taking pictures and your hands won't be free to pick up food.

Memorial Day

Because creamy picnic side dishes damage a diet much more than the main course does, skip the calorie-dense potato and macaroni salads in favor of a 59-calorie ear of corn on the cob, advises Robyn Flipse, RD, author of *Fighting the Freshman Fifteen*.

June

Flag Day

Salute the Stars and Stripes by celebrating local berry season. Instead of piling the berries on a high-calorie, high-sat-fat shortcake, choose the ripest fruit to stir into creamy fat-free plain yogurt. Not only is yogurt easy to digest, it works as well as milk and cheese in cutting pounds, a University of Tennessee study found. Eighteen women who ate 500 fewer calories and 6 ounces of yogurt three times a day for 12 weeks lost 3.6 more pounds and 1.2 more inches from their waists than 16 women who also cut calories but ate no yogurt.

Father's Day

Serve Dad's dinner in courses rather than presenting it all at once, says Will Clower, PhD, author of *The Fat Fallacy:* "Eating more slowly will give your body the 15 or so minutes it takes to register that it's full." Suggested menu of 511 calories: Start with salad, move on to shrimp cocktail, follow it with a small steak with mushrooms and steamed veggies, and end with fruit and pudding.

vegetarian or "semi-vegetarian" and ate fish or eggs were half as likely as meat eaters to be overweight. Vegans were two-thirds less likely than meat eaters to be overweight.

May

Mother's Day

On the country's most popular day to dine out, make your reservation at a gourmet restaurant that serves reasonably sized portions of ultra-satisfying food, suggests Carrie Wiatt, a celebrity clinical nutritionist based in Culver City, California. By way of comparison: The sea bass with potato and leeks at Daniel, an acclaimed restaurant in New York City, has about 630 calories; a platter of fried shrimp, scallops, clam strips, and fish fillets at Red Lobster, up to 1,060 calories.

Graduation Party

Bring a camera and act as the "official photographer." It can be part of your gift to the guest of honor. Your mind will be

Baby Shower

Have a bowl of satisfying soup—hot or cold—before you go. In a recent Pennsylvania State University study of nearly 150 dieters, those who consumed 200 calories' worth of soup before lunch and dinner every day lost 5 pounds more after a year than those who ate 200 calories of low-fat but salty snacks as an appetizer.

July

Independence Day

Lay off the lemonade. We know the weather's hot, but a recent study at Penn State showed that when women consumed 156 calories' worth of nonalcoholic beverages with a meal, they only slightly adjusted their food intake and ended up still consuming 104 calories in addition to their meal. Better choice: sparkling water with a few raspberries dropped in.

Neighborhood Picnic

So you don't feel like a blob after the block party, limit the damage with a jaunt before you go. Researchers at the University of Glasgow in Scotland measured the triglycerides, or blood fat, of 20 men after they splurged on a high-fat feast of whipped cream, nuts, and chocolate. Normally, even one fatty meal can spike triglyceride levels, which can raise your heart disease risk. Though the subjects consumed more than a day's worth of fat in one sitting, their triglyceride levels rose 25 percent less when they walked for 90 minutes before bingeing than when they didn't.

August

Wedding Reception

Before you leave, eat two fat-free hot dogs without the buns and carry a clutch purse when you head out the door. Together, they will wipe out your desire and ability to stuff yourself with hors d'oeuvres. Think about it: Who wants pigs in a blanket after polishing off two franks? You won't have a hand free for food anyway, what with a clutch purse in one hand and a 50-calorie wine spritzer in the other.

Summer Vacation

Request that the minibar in your hotel room be emptied, and stock it yourself with water, milk, 100-percent juice, low-fat yogurt, and fruit. You can enjoy breakfast in your room every morning and avoid the pancakes, French toast, and omelets at the hotel's overpriced buffet.

September

Labor Day

Focus on the recreational activities—volleyball, swimming, or softball—far away from the picnic table. Be among the last to begin eating, so when it's

time to jump back into the lake or pick up the game, you'll have finished only one plateful.

Back to School

Buy your kids' snacks and treats in preportioned bags and store them out of sight to resist reaching for them. Distance makes a difference: In one study, when women had to walk six feet for a chocolate kiss, they ate five fewer of them than when the bowl was on their desk.

October

Columbus Day

Don't go overboard with Italian-sausage-meatball-and-provolone sandwiches. Toast the Italian explorer with a glass of tomato juice spiked with hot red-pepper sauce (both tomatoes and chiles were discovered in the New World). Dutch researchers found that subjects ate 10 to 16 percent less after consuming red pepper in a capsule with tomato juice, 30 minutes before eating. Hot pepper stimulates nerves in the mouth as

well as in the stomach, the scientists think, making you feel satisfied with less food.

Birthday Party

Pop a strong breath strip in your mouth when you arrive to stave off a taste for nibble foods. Spare yourself at least 100 calories by opting for a slice from the middle of the sheet cake rather than an overly frosted (and undoubtedly overly sweet) end piece.

Halloween

Give trinkets as treats, and you won't be haunted by chocolate. The kids won't mind as much as you may think. When Yale researchers allowed 3- to 14-year-old trick-or-treaters to choose between a piece of candy and a small toy such as a pencil or ball, half took the toy. But if Halloween isn't the same without candy, handing out fun-size packs of Raisinets (67 calories) or rolls of Smarties (25 calories) are your best bets. Don't buy the assorted packages of candy because you'll be tempted to try one of every kind.

November

Tailgate Party

Don't sabotage your weight loss just for the sake of your team. Carry a nutrient-rich chilled pumpkin smoothie in a thermos to sip *before* the pre-game feast. It's a strong defense against hunger pangs. Use convenient canned pumpkin, which has more fiber and carotenoids than fresh cooked. Blend 1 tablespoon pumpkin with ½ cup of low-fat milk, half a banana, and a dash of cinnamon.

Thanksgiving

Don't eat the veggies! If the green beans are buried under that creamy mushroom sauce and the sweet potatoes are oozing with glaze or marshmallows, fill half your plate with skinless turkey breast, top it with cranberries (an antioxidant powerhouse), and take miniportions of other items you love and get only once a year, suggests New York City culinary consultant Jackie Newgent, RD. Total calories for 6 ounces of turkey; 2 tablespoons each of cranberry sauce, stuffing, and mashed potatoes; and a sliver of corn bread: 471.

Black Friday

As you kick off the holiday shopping season, skip the high-cal, high-fat mall snacks. Instead, order a kid's meal with fruit rather than fries. You'll get a more reasonable portion size for an adult, plus you can use the toy as a stocking stuffer.

December

Holiday Parties

Don't put more than two foods on your plate at one time. "The variety of foods at holiday parties prompts you to overeat. This plan forces you to decide early on what you most want to try," says Cornell University's Dr. Wansink. "Chances are, you'll be satisfied after just one refill."

Christmas

Don't waste 300 or 400 calories nibbling on food while you're cooking. Before you prepare the meal, make yourself an 80-calorie plate of crudités—4 whole wheat crackers; 1 large celery rib, sliced; 5 baby carrots; and 1 teaspoon ranch dressing. For sipping, fill your wine glass with sparkling water and a slice of lime.

New Year's Eve

Ring in the New Year with classic champagne. Each 90-calorie glass is a diet bargain compared with a margarita (327 calories) or any other sugar-filled mixed drink. And be sure to raise your glass of bubbly in a celebratory toast to the new you!

Salads and Soups

SALADS

SOUPS

Zesty Summer Salad

—Angelica Persson, Loxley, Alabama

60 Calories

Angelica likes to make this with organic veggies and the small, knobby, green Vidalia onions you find in markets in the spring. We used scallions.

Prep time: 5 minutes
Chill time: 4 hours

  3 **large tomatoes, cut into wedges**
  1 **hothouse cucumber, cut into 1" pieces**
  3 to 4 **scallions, thinly sliced**
  ¼ **cup light Italian dressing**
     Ground black pepper
  6 **lettuce leaves**
  6 **tablespoons grated Parmesan cheese**

In a refrigerator container, combine the tomatoes, cucumber, and scallions. Add the dressing, and season to taste with salt and pepper; mix well. Cover and refrigerate for 4 hours or overnight, stirring the salad several times.

To serve, drain off most of the dressing. Place a lettuce leaf on each of 6 salad plates and spoon salad into each leaf. Sprinkle 1 tablespoon Parmesan over each.

Makes 6 servings

Per serving: *60 calories, 3 g protein, 7 g carbohydrate, 3 g fat, 5 mg cholesterol, 220 mg sodium, 2 g fiber*

Diet Exchanges: *0 milk, 1 vegetable, 0 fruit, 0 bread, ½ meat, ½ fat*

½ **Carb Choice**

SHOPPING SAVVY

Top Tomatoes

Love "real" tomatoes but hate to wait for summer? Give new Campari tomatoes a try. Brilliant red, ripe, juicy, and sweet (balanced with a little acidity), they taste like summer tomatoes year-round. Campari tomatoes are grown without pesticides and are hand-picked when ripe. And like all tomatoes, they're a good source of important nutrients, including lycopene and vitamins A and C. Wedge them for salads, dice for bruschetta, slice for sandwiches and pizza, and chop for pasta. Sold in supermarkets across the country.

90 Calories

Nutty Fruit Salad

—Angelica de Koning, Santa Clara, California

Toast the pecans in a toaster oven or on the stove top first, if you like.
Toasting adds crunch and brings out the flavor.

Prep time: 15 minutes

3 cups shredded iceberg lettuce

3 cups mixed spring greens

1 large pear, sliced

1 cup drained canned pineapple tidbits
or diced fresh pineapple

1 blood or navel orange, peeled and
sectioned

¼ cup dried cranberries or raisins

¼ cup sliced natural almonds

2 tablespoons coarsely chopped pecans

⅓ cup light raspberry vinaigrette

In a large bowl, combine the iceberg lettuce, greens, pear, pineapple, and orange.

Sprinkle with the cranberries or raisins, almonds, and pecans, and drizzle with the dressing. Toss well.

Makes 4 servings

Per serving: *90 calories, 4 g protein, 28 g carbohydrate, 9 g fat, 0 mg cholesterol, 170 mg sodium, 6 g fiber*

Diet Exchanges: *0 milk, ½ vegetable, 1½ fruit, 0 bread, 0 meat, ½ fat*

2 Carb Choices

Bulgur Salad

230 Calories

—Rosalyn Minassian, Burlington, Massachusetts

"I like to serve this as a side dish or main course, especially during the hot summer months when I make it at least once a week. For a change, spoon the fiber-rich salad into hollowed-out tomatoes."

Prep time: 10 minutes
Standing time: 20 minutes
Cook time: 27 minutes

BULGUR

2 tablespoons canola oil
1 large red onion, chopped
1 can (14½ ounces) diced tomatoes
½ cup water
1 cup fine bulgur
¼ cup lemon juice
Salt
Ground black pepper

GARNISH

¼ cup chopped red or green bell pepper
¼ cup thinly sliced scallions
¼ cup peeled and chopped cucumber
2 tablespoons finely chopped fresh flat-leaf parsley

To make the bulgur: In a heavy medium saucepan over medium heat, warm the oil. Add the onion and cook, stirring often, about 6 minutes, or until tender. Add the tomatoes (with juice), and bring to a boil. Reduce the heat to low, add the water, and simmer, uncovered, for 5 minutes, or until lightly thickened. Remove from the heat.

Stir in the bulgur and lemon juice, and season to taste with salt and pepper. Cover and let stand for 15 to 20 minutes, or until the liquid has been absorbed and the bulgur is tender.

To make the garnish: In a medium bowl, mix the bell pepper, scallions, cucumber, and parsley. Stir half into the bulgur, and mound the mixture on a platter. Spoon the remaining garnish on top.

Makes 4 servings

Per serving: *230 calories, 6 g protein, 38 g carbohydrate, 8 g fat, 0 mg cholesterol, 360 mg sodium, 8 g fiber*

Diet Exchanges: *0 milk, 1½ vegetable, 0 fruit, 1½ bread, 0 meat, 1½ fat*

2½ Carb Choices

Suzanne's Toasted Bulgur and Dill Salad

—Suzanne Vandyck, Santa Clara, California

Suzanne learned about this salad from a Turkish friend. It satisfies her appetite and keeps her cravings at bay. You can use chopped fresh parsley or cilantro instead of the dill.

Prep time: 10 minutes
Cook time: 22 minutes
Standing time: 30 minutes

1½ **cups medium bulgur**
  3 **cups water or reduced-sodium, fat-free vegetable or chicken broth**
  ½ **teaspoon salt**
  ½ **cup snipped fresh dill**
  ½ **cup chopped scallions or red onion (optional)**
  ¼ **cup lemon juice, or to taste**
  2 **tablespoons extra virgin olive oil**
  1 **teaspoon ground sweet paprika**
  ⅛ **to ¼ teaspoon ground red pepper**

In a heavy medium skillet over medium-high heat, toast the bulgur, stirring occasionally, about 8 minutes, or until lightly browned and "popping." Transfer to a bowl.

In a heavy medium saucepan over high heat, bring the water or broth to a boil. Stir in the toasted bulgur and salt, and return to a boil. Reduce the heat to low, cover, and simmer about 12 minutes, or until the liquid has been absorbed and the bulgur is tender.

Remove from the heat and let stand, covered, for 10 minutes.

Transfer to a large salad bowl, cover loosely with waxed paper, and let stand (or refrigerate) until cooled to room temperature. Stir in the dill, scallions or red onion (if using), lemon juice, oil, paprika, and ground red pepper.

Makes 6 servings

Per serving: *160 calories, 4 g protein, 26 g carbohydrate, 5 g fat, 0 mg cholesterol, 200 mg sodium, 6 g fiber*

Diet Exchanges: *0 milk, 0 vegetable, 0 fruit, 1½ bread, 0 meat, 1 fat*

2 Carb Choices

Spicy Tuna Salad Mix

140 Calories

—Morgan Riggan, Nanaimo, British Columbia, Canada

"This recipe has all the flavor of normal tuna salad without all the fat. The Dijon mustard gives it that creamy texture that usually comes from lots of mayo. I really enjoy spicy food, so I use hot salsa and hot sauce, but mild salsa will do. The salsa just gives flavor and bulks up the final product."

Prep time: 5 minutes

1 can (12 ounces) water-packed light tuna, drained and flaked

½ cup mild, medium, or hot chunky salsa

¼ cup chopped red onion

3 tablespoons reduced-fat mayonnaise

1 large dill pickle, chopped

1 tablespoon Dijon mustard

Tabasco to taste (optional)

Salt

Ground black pepper

In a medium bowl, mix together the tuna, salsa, red onion, mayonnaise, pickle, mustard, and Tabasco, if using. Season to taste with salt and pepper.

Makes 4 servings

Per serving: *140 calories, 23 g protein, 7 g carbohydrate, 2.5 g fat, 25 mg cholesterol, 870 mg sodium, 1 g fiber*

Diet Exchanges: *0 milk, 1 vegetable, 0 fruit, 0 bread, 0 meat, ½ fat*

½ **Carb Choice**

Summer Antipasto Salad

—Kristin Sheppard, Collingswood, NJ

All of the essentials for this (almost) no-cook meal are easily found in your supermarket.

Prep time: 20 minutes
Blanch time: 5 minutes

D R E S S I N G

   3 tablespoons red wine vinegar or balsamic vinegar

   2 tablespoons olive oil

   ½ clove garlic, minced

   ⅛ teaspoon dried basil

   ⅛ teaspoon salt

   ⅛ teaspoon ground black pepper

S A L A D

   1 small bunch broccoli, cut into florets

   1 medium zucchini, cut into 2" matchsticks

   1 pound shrimp, cooked

   1 cup cherry tomatoes, halved

   ½ cup canned artichoke hearts, drained and quartered

   ⅓ cup pitted kalamata olives, pitted

   4 ounces part-skim mozzarella cheese, cut into ½" cubes

   8 slices reduced-fat deli ham, rolled into tubes

   16 slices turkey pepperoni

To make the dressing: In a small bowl whisk together the red wine or balsamic vinegar, oil, garlic, basil, salt, and black pepper.

To make the salad: Bring a medium saucepan of water to a boil. Fill a large bowl with ice water and set near the stove. Working in batches, boil the broccoli and zucchini just until tender (they will turn bright green). Use a slotted spoon to transfer the vegetables to the ice water to halt the cooking process. Drain well.

Place the shrimp in the center of a large platter. Arrange the broccoli, zucchini, tomatoes, artichoke hearts, olives, cheese, ham, and pepperoni in small mounds around the shrimp. Drizzle with the dressing.

Makes 4 servings

Per serving: *260 calories, 27 g protein, 9 g carbohydrate, 13 g fat, 135 mg cholesterol, 770 mg sodium, 3 g fiber*

Diet Exchanges: *0 milk, 1 vegetable, 0 fruit, 0 bread, 2 meat, 1 fat*

1 Carb Choice

350 Calories

Chili-Grilled Chicken Salad

—Rene Collins, Clute, Texas

"Salad as a meal can serve any nice low-fat, good-carb plan. By adding black beans and corn, you increase the carbs slightly, but also add protein, fiber, and flavor."

Prep time: 10 minutes
Grill time: 8 minutes

DRESSING

¼ cup light ranch dressing

¼ cup mild green salsa

1 to 2 tablespoons chopped fresh cilantro

SALAD

1 tablespoon chili powder

¼ teaspoon ground cumin

¼ teaspoon garlic powder

¼ teaspoon onion powder

¼ teaspoon salt

⅛ teaspoon ground black pepper

1 pound thin chicken breast slices or chicken tenders

1 lime, quartered

6 cups shredded romaine lettuce

1 can (15 ounces) black beans, rinsed and drained

½ cup corn kernels

1 medium tomato, chopped

¼ cup thinly sliced red onion

To make the dressing: In a small bowl, mix the ranch dressing, salsa, and cilantro until blended. Cover and refrigerate.

To make the salad: Coat a barbecue grill or ridged grill pan with olive oil spray, and heat to medium-hot. In a cup, mix the chili powder, cumin, garlic powder, onion powder, salt, and pepper. Rub evenly on both sides of the chicken.

Grill the chicken, turning once, for 3 to 4 minutes, or until it is no longer pink and the juices run clear. Transfer to a plate. Squeeze the lime over the cooked chicken.

In a large bowl, toss the romaine with half the dressing. Divide among 4 plates.

Sprinkle the beans, corn, tomato, and red onion equally over each serving and top with the grilled chicken. Serve the remaining dressing on the side.

Makes 4 servings

Per serving: *350 calories, 42 g protein, 23 g carbohydrate, 9 g fat, 100 mg cholesterol, 740 mg sodium, 8 g fiber*

Diet Exchanges: *0 milk, 1 vegetable, 0 fruit, 1 bread, 5½ meat, 1 fat*

1½ Carb Choices

Hawaiian Chicken Salad

—Diann Garnett, Bethlehem, Pennsylvania

350 Calories

This sunny, vibrant salad can be served warm or at room temperature.

Prep time: 15 minutes
Cook time: 40 minutes for rice (unless using cooked rice)

D R E S S I N G

1 can (8 ounces) pineapple chunks (packed in juice), drained, ⅓ cup juice reserved

3 tablespoons extra virgin olive oil

⅛ teaspoon salt

⅛ teaspoon ground black pepper

S A L A D

¾ pound boneless, skinless chicken breast halves, grilled and cut into cubes

1½ cups cooked brown rice

1 red bell pepper, chopped

½ cup red onion, finely chopped

4 large lettuce leaves

2 tablespoons chopped pistachios

To make the dressing: Reserve the pineapple chunks for the salad. In a small bowl, stir the ⅓ cup pineapple juice with the oil, salt, and pepper.

To make the salad: In a medium bowl, combine the reserved pineapple chunks, chicken, rice, bell pepper, and red onion. Add the dressing and toss gently to mix.

Arrange the lettuce leaves on 4 plates. Top with the salad and sprinkle with the pistachios.

Makes 4 servings

Per serving: *350 calories, 23 g protein, 31 g carbohydrate, 14 g fat, 50 mg cholesterol, 135 mg sodium, 3 g fiber*

Diet Exchanges: *0 milk, 1 vegetable, ½ fruit, 1 bread, 3 meat, 2 fat*

2 Carb Choices

240 Calories

Blue-Cheese Chicken-Taco Salad

—Chris Detris, Breinigsville, Pennsylvania

Using blue cheese instead of the more traditional Cheddar in this salad adds an extra-rich kick of flavor.

Prep time: 15 minutes
Cook time: 12 minutes

½ cup reduced-fat ranch dressing

2 tablespoons medium-spicy green salsa

1 tablespoon canola oil

¾ pound boneless, skinless chicken breast halves, cut into ½" pieces

1 small jalapeño chile pepper, finely chopped (wear plastic gloves when handling)

2 teaspoons fajita seasoning

8 cups torn romaine lettuce

1 can (15 ounces) pinto beans, rinsed and drained

1 large tomato, chopped

2 scallions, thinly sliced

1 cup crumbled baked tortilla chips

½ cup crumbled blue cheese

1 tablespoon chopped cilantro

In a small bowl, mix the ranch dressing and salsa.

In a large nonstick skillet over medium heat, warm the oil. Add the chicken and sprinkle with the jalapeño pepper. Cook, stirring frequently, for 8 to 10 minutes, or until the chicken is no longer pink in the thickest part. Sprinkle with the fajita seasoning and cook 1 minute longer.

In a large bowl, toss the warm chicken mixture with the romaine, pinto beans, tomato, and scallions. Add the salsa dressing and toss to coat. Add the tortilla chips and blue cheese, and gently toss again. Sprinkle with the cilantro.

Makes 6 servings

Per serving: *240 calories, 19 g protein, 20 g carbohydrate, 9 g fat, 40 mg cholesterol, 570 mg sodium, 5 g fiber*

Diet Exchanges: *0 milk, 1 vegetable, 0 fruit, 1 bread, 2 meat, 1½ fat*

1 Carb Choice

50 Calories

Southern Salad

—Mel Roland, Savannah, Tennessee

"Salads get very boring and this adds a little zing!"

Prep time: 5 minutes

3 tablespoons reduced-fat mayonnaise
1 tablespoon fresh lemon juice
   Pinch garlic powder
   Salt
   Cracked black pepper
1 bag (5 ounces) torn romaine lettuce
1 box grape tomatoes, halved
1 cup matchstick-cut carrots (from a bag)

In a salad bowl, blend the mayonnaise, lemon juice, and garlic powder. Season to taste with salt and pepper. Add the romaine, grape tomatoes, and carrots, and toss to mix well.

Makes 4 servings

Per serving: *50 calories, 1 g protein, 9 g carbohydrate, 2 g fat, 0 mg cholesterol, 200 mg sodium, 2 g fiber*

Diet Exchanges: *0 milk, 1½ vegetable, 0 fruit, 0 bread, 0 meat, ½ fat*

½ **Carb Choice**

Healthy Bean Salad

—Karen Johnson, Sarnia, Ontario, Canada

"It is tasty, satisfying, and full of vitamins and iron."

150 Calories

Prep time: 5 minutes
Chill time: 1 hour

- 1 can (14½ ounces) green bean and wax bean combo, drained
- 1 cup canned kidney beans, rinsed and drained
- 1 large tomato, chopped
- ½ hothouse cucumber, chopped
- ½ small red onion, chopped
- 2 tablespoons extra virgin olive oil
- 2 tablespoons balsamic vinegar
- 1 tablespoon chopped fresh basil or ½ teaspoon dried
- 1 tablespoon chopped fresh parsley
  Salt
  Ground black pepper

In a large bowl, mix the bean combo, kidney beans, tomato, cucumber, red onion, oil, vinegar, basil, and parsley. Season to taste with salt and pepper. Cover and refrigerate for 1 hour.

Makes 4 servings

Per serving: *150 calories, 5 g protein, 18 g carbohydrate, 8 g fat, 0 mg cholesterol, 330 mg sodium, 5 g fiber*

Diet Exchanges: *0 milk, 1 vegetable, 0 fruit, 1 bread, 0 meat, 1½ fat*

1 Carb Choice

290 Calories Maple-Glazed Asian Salmon Salad

—Elizabeth Janelle, Arlington, Virginia

Prep time: 15 minutes
Cook time: 24 minutes

S A L M O N

2 tablespoons reduced-sodium soy sauce
1 tablespoon maple syrup
1 teaspoon Asian toasted sesame oil
½ teaspoon grated fresh ginger
4 skinless salmon fillets (12 ounces)

D R E S S I N G

2 tablespoons reduced-sodium soy sauce
1 tablespoon maple syrup
1 tablespoon rice vinegar
2 teaspoons canola oil
1½ teaspoons Asian toasted sesame oil
1½ teaspoons Dijon mustard
1½ teaspoons grated fresh ginger
¼ teaspoon chili paste

S A L A D

8 cups torn romaine lettuce
1 cup bean sprouts
1 small red bell pepper, sliced into thin strips
1 cup snow peas, stringed and sliced diagonally into 1" pieces
1 cup white button mushrooms, thinly sliced
2 scallions, thinly sliced
½ cup chow mein noodles (optional)

To make the salmon: In a shallow dish, mix the soy sauce, maple syrup, sesame oil, and ginger. Coat a ridged grill pan with olive oil spray and warm over medium-high heat. Turn the salmon in the soy mixture to coat both sides. Grill the salmon, turning once and brushing with remaining soy sauce mixture, about 8 minutes, or until just opaque in the thickest part. Transfer to a plate.

To make the dressing: In a large bowl, whisk together the soy sauce, maple syrup, rice vinegar, canola and sesame oils, mustard, ginger, and chili paste.

To make the salad: Add the romaine, bean sprouts, bell pepper, snow peas, mushrooms, and scallions to the dressing. Toss to coat. Arrange the salad on 4 plates and top each with a piece of salmon. Sprinkle with chow mein noodles, if desired.

Makes 4 servings

Per serving: *290 calories, 22 g protein, 18 g carbohydrate, 15 g fat, 50 mg cholesterol, 690 mg sodium, 4 g fiber*

Diet Exchanges: *0 milk, 1½ vegetable, 0 fruit, ½ bread, 2½ meat, 1½ fat*

1 Carb Choice

170 Calories

Easy and Light Seafood Salad

—Mary Savannah, Butler, Pennsylvania

"This recipe is flavorful, easy, and makes me feel like I'm not even dieting."

Prep time: 10 minutes
Chill time: 1 hour

- ½ cup light sour cream
- ½ cup chopped sweet onion
- ½ cup chopped fresh cilantro
- 1 can (4½ ounces) chopped mild green chiles, drained
- 2 tablespoons lime juice
  Salt
  Ground black pepper
- 1 pound medium shrimp, cooked or lump crabmeat
- 1 bag (5 ounces) mixed baby greens
  Lime wedges

In a large bowl, mix the sour cream, onion, cilantro, chiles, and lime juice. Season to taste with salt and pepper.

Add the shrimp or crabmeat and fold in gently with a rubber spatula. Cover and refrigerate for 1 hour to blend the flavors. Serve on a bed of mixed greens with lime wedges to squeeze over top.

Makes 4 servings

Per serving: *170 calories, 22 g protein, 9 g carbohydrate, 5 g fat, 160 mg cholesterol, 510 mg sodium, 2 g fiber*

Diet Exchanges: *0 milk, 1 vegetable, 0 fruit, 0 bread, 3 meat, 1 fat*

½ **Carb Choice**

130 Calories

Zesty Corn Salad

—Linda Chaput, North Bay, Ontario, Canada

This flavorful dish is a great way to start a meal, but is equally appealing when served as a side dish!

Prep time: 15 minutes
Cook time: 5 minutes
Chill time: 30 minutes

  1 **package (10 ounces) frozen corn kernels, cooked and drained**
½ **cup chopped celery**
½ **cup thinly sliced white button mushrooms**
¼ **cup chopped scallions**
¼ **cup chopped red bell pepper**
  2 **tablespoons olive oil**
  2 **tablespoons red wine vinegar**
  1 **tablespoon Splenda**
  1 **tablespoon water**
½ **teaspoon mustard powder**
⅛ **teaspoon garlic salt**
   Salt
   Ground black pepper

In a large salad bowl, combine the corn, celery, mushrooms, scallions, and bell pepper. In a cup, mix the oil, vinegar, Splenda, water, mustard, and garlic salt. Pour over the corn mixture, season to taste with salt and pepper, and stir to mix.

Cover and refrigerate at least 30 minutes, or until ready to serve.

Makes 4 servings

Per serving: *130 calories, 3 g protein, 16 g carbohydrate, 7 g fat, 0 mg cholesterol, 50 mg sodium, 2 g fiber*

Diet Exchanges: *0 milk, ½ vegetable, 0 fruit, 1 bread, 0 meat, 1½ fat*

1 Carb Choice

40 Calories

Mustard Salad Dressing

—Carol Lambert, Cincinnati, Ohio

Not only is this salad dressing low in carbs and calories, but it also makes a great low-fat substitute for full-fat honey-mustard dressing.

Prep time: 5 minutes

- ¼ cup reduced-fat mayonnaise or salad dressing
- 1½ tablespoons rice vinegar or white vinegar
- 1 tablespoon Splenda
- 1 teaspoon Dijon mustard

In a small bowl, whisk the mayonnaise or dressing, vinegar, Splenda, and mustard. Serve with cut-up vegetables for dipping or toss with a garden salad.

Makes 5 servings (⅓ cup), 1 generous tablespoon each

Per serving: *40 calories, 0 g protein, 2 g carbohydrate, 4 g fat, 5 mg cholesterol, 125 mg sodium, 0 g fiber*

Diet Exchanges: *0 milk, 0 vegetable, 0 fruit, 0 bread, 0 meat, 1 fat*

0 Carb Choices

SECRETS OF WEIGHT-LOSS WINNERS

• I keep myself motivated by staying with the weight-loss program to the end. I know I will benefit from it at the end if I stick with it now. Mind over matter!

—Catherine Brown, Lakefield, Ontario, Canada

• Egg whites and applesauce are good substitutes in many baking recipes, in place of whole eggs and oil.

—Staisha White, Toledo, Oregon

• Drink a 16-ounce bottle of very cold water before lunch and dinner; it will cut down your appetite. That way you eat what you need and do not get stuffed.

—Staisha White, Toledo, Oregon

150 Calories

Cream of Cabbage Soup

—Ed Izsak, Kipling, Saskatchewan, Canada

"A filling soup with great potential for weight loss! Tastes good, too."

Prep time: 15 minutes
Cook time: 27 minutes

2 cups reduced-sodium, fat-free chicken broth

1 head green cabbage, cored and coarsely chopped

3 carrots, sliced

1 large onion, chopped

2 ribs celery, sliced

1 teaspoon dried thyme

½ teaspoon salt

¼ teaspoon ground black pepper

3 tablespoons trans-free margarine

⅓ cup all-purpose flour

4 cups 1% milk

In a large saucepan or Dutch oven, combine the broth, cabbage, carrots, onion, celery, thyme, salt, and pepper. Cover and bring to a boil over high heat. Reduce the heat to low and simmer about 15 minutes, or until the vegetables are tender.

Meanwhile, in a medium nonstick saucepan over medium heat, melt the margarine. Stir in the flour and cook, stirring, 1 minute. Gradually whisk in the milk. Bring to a boil, whisking often. Reduce the heat and simmer, stirring often, about 5 minutes, or until thickened.

Pour the milk mixture into the cabbage mixture. Bring to a simmer over medium heat, and cook about 5 minutes, stirring often, until the soup is lightly thickened.

Makes 8 servings

Per serving: *150 calories, 7 g protein, 19 g carbohydrate, 5 g fat, 5 mg cholesterol, 310 mg sodium, 3 g fiber*

Diet Exchanges: *½ milk, ½ vegetable, 0 fruit, ½ bread, 0 meat, 1 fat*

1 Carb Choice

The Best Black Bean–Turkey Chili

350 Calories

—Mimi Lenio, Palm Coast, Florida

"Top with reduced-fat Mexican cheese and serve with cornbread. It's yummy. A small bowl of this chili is extremely satisfying!"

Prep time: 15 minutes
Cook time: 40 minutes

  1 tablespoon olive oil

1½ pounds lean ground turkey breast

  2 hot chile peppers, minced (wear plastic gloves when handling)

  1 large onion, chopped

  6 cloves garlic, thinly sliced

  2 tablespoons chili powder

  2 teaspoons ground cumin

  2 teaspoons dried oregano

  ⅛ to ½ teaspoon ground red pepper

    Salt

    Ground black pepper

  2 cans (15 ounces each) black beans, rinsed and drained

  2 cans (14½ ounces each) no-salt-added diced tomatoes

  1 can (14½ ounces) reduced-sodium, fat-free chicken broth

 25 pitted prunes, chopped

In a large, deep nonstick skillet or Dutch oven over medium-high heat, warm the oil. Add the ground turkey, hot peppers, onion, garlic, chili powder, cumin, oregano, and red pepper. Season to taste with salt and black pepper. Cook, breaking turkey up with the back of a spoon, for 10 to 12 minutes, or until the turkey is lightly browned.

Stir in the black beans, tomatoes (with juice), broth, and prunes. Bring to a boil. Reduce the heat to low and simmer, uncovered, about 30 minutes, or until thickened and flavorful.

Makes 6 servings

Per serving: *350 calories, 36 g protein, 50 g carbohydrate, 6 g fat, 45 mg cholesterol, 700 mg sodium, 11 g fiber*

Diet Exchanges: *0 milk, 1½ vegetable, 1 fruit, 1 bread, 3½ meat, ½ fat*

3 Carb Choices

Southwest Chicken Soup

—Sharon Murphy, Chicago, Illinois

This low-calorie soup is a great way to start a meal!

Prep time: 10 minutes
Cook time: 15 minutes

1 can (15 ounces) black beans, rinsed and drained

1 can (14½ ounces) reduced-sodium, fat-free chicken broth

1 container (12 ounces) fresh medium-spicy salsa

1 can (10 ounces) chunk chicken, drained and broken into pieces

1 cup corn kernels

2 teaspoons ground cumin

1½ teaspoons chili powder

4 tablespoons shredded reduced-fat Cheddar cheese (optional)

4 tablespoons fat-free sour cream (optional)

¼ cup chopped fresh cilantro (optional)

In a large, heavy saucepan over medium-high heat, stir together the beans, broth, salsa, chicken, corn, cumin, and chili powder. Bring to a boil. Reduce the heat to low, cover, and simmer for 15 minutes to blend the flavors.

Ladle the soup into four bowls and, if you like, top each with 1 tablespoon Cheddar, 1 tablespoon sour cream, and some cilantro.

Makes 4 servings

Per serving: *230 calories, 6 g protein, 19 g carbohydrate, 6 g fat, 35 mg cholesterol, 980 mg sodium, 6 g fiber*

Diet Exchanges: *0 milk, 0 vegetable, 0 fruit, 1 bread, 2 meat, 0 fat*

2 Carb Choices

60 Calories

Gazpacho

—Jill Davies, Abbotsford, British Columbia, Canada

"This recipe is my own creation which I have improved on over the years. The addition of balsamic vinegar is optional but I found it really brightens the fresh flavor of the tomatoes."

Prep time: 15 minutes
Chill time: 2 hours

- 5 large tomatoes, peeled (see Kitchen Tip) and chopped
- 1½ cups chopped, peeled hothouse cucumber
- 1 large red bell pepper, chopped
- 2 ribs celery, chopped
- 1 small white onion, chopped
- 2 cloves garlic, minced
- ¾ cup reduced-sodium tomato juice
- 1 cup reduced-sodium, fat-free beef broth
- ¼ cup chopped fresh parsley, plus sprigs for garnish
- 1 tablespoon balsamic vinegar (optional)
- 2 dashes Tabasco sauce
  Salt
  Ground black pepper

Reserve some chopped tomato and cucumber for garnish. In a food processor, in batches, pulse the remaining tomatoes and cucumber with the bell pepper, celery, onion, and garlic to a chunky puree. Add tomato juice as needed to thin the mixture.

Transfer to a large bowl or container, and stir in any remaining tomato juice, the broth, parsley, vinegar (if using), and Tabasco. Season to taste with salt and pepper. Cover and refrigerate at least 2 hours, or until ready to serve.

Ladle into bowls and top with the reserved chopped tomato and cucumber and a sprig of parsley.

Makes 6 servings

Per serving: *60 calories, 2 g protein, 12 g carbohydrate, 0 g fat, 0 mg cholesterol, 45 mg sodium, 3 g fiber*

Diet Exchanges: *0 milk, 2 vegetable, 0 fruit, 0 bread, 0 meat, 0 fat*

1 Carb Choice

Kitchen Tip

To peel the tomatoes, plunge them one at a time into a saucepan of boiling water, and cook for about 30 seconds. Remove with a slotted spoon. Cool, core, and slip off the skins.

Healthy Hamburger and Veggie Soup

—Christy Weller, Nelsonville, Ohio

190 Calories

You get a great dose of good-for-you veggies in one soothing bowl of this favorite soup.

Prep time: 15 minutes
Cook time: 30 minutes

¾ **pound ground beef sirloin**
1 **medium onion, chopped**
1 **teaspoon Italian dried herb seasoning**
½ **teaspoon salt**
½ **teaspoon ground black pepper**
1 **can (14½ ounces) diced tomatoes**
2 **cans (14½ ounces each) reduced-sodium, fat-free beef broth**
1 **cup reduced-sodium tomato juice**
1 **cup frozen mixed peas and carrots**
1 **cup frozen cut green beans**
1 **cup frozen baby lima beans**
1 **cup frozen corn kernels**
½ **cup cooked brown rice**
1 **tablespoon Worcestershire sauce**

In a medium nonstick skillet over medium-high heat, crumble the ground sirloin. Sprinkle in the onion, Italian seasoning, salt, and pepper. Cook, breaking up the beef with the back of a spoon, about 10 minutes, or until the beef is browned. Drain in a colander, if necessary. Transfer to a Dutch oven.

Stir the tomatoes (with their juice), broth, tomato juice, peas and carrots, green beans, lima beans, corn, and rice into the beef. Bring to a boil over high heat. Reduce the heat to low, cover, and simmer about 20 minutes, or until the vegetables are tender and the flavors have blended. Stir in the Worcestershire.

Makes 6 servings

Per serving: *190 calories, 17 g protein, 22 g carbohydrate, 3.5 g fat, 25 mg cholesterol, 700 mg sodium, 4 g fiber*

Diet Exchanges: *0 milk, 2 vegetable, 0 fruit, ½ bread, 2 meat, ½ fat*

1½ Carb Choices

It Worked for Me!

Evelyn Gross

VITAL STATS

Weight lost: 85 pounds

Time to goal: 18 months

Amazing results: I can fit in airplane seats, dining chairs, and stadium seats again!

Evelyn had worn a size 24 for about 15 years. The extra weight wasn't really a problem for her—until her husband experienced frightening complications from diabetes-related surgery. At that point, Evelyn knew her eating habits had to change in order for both of them to get—and stay—healthy for the long term.

"My daughter is really my inspiration. As she grows into a terrific young lady, I want to be sure that I'm around to see what her life has in store. I wouldn't want to miss that. Combined with worries about my husband's health, that was all the motivation I needed to make some changes.

"I learned to cook healthier for myself and my husband. We used to eat out probably five times a week, but when you do that you have no idea what you're really getting on that plate. Weight Watchers taught me to read labels and to understand how carbs, calories, and fiber work together. I can't say I love cooking, but now I know we're eating healthy, and that's important to me.

"Daily exercise has also become a big part of my life. I walk for 45 minutes every day—and here in Virginia that can mean getting up pretty early to beat the heat. But I prefer to work out in the morning because then it's done and I can check it off my list. I also wear a pedometer and aim for 10,000 steps every day. I even managed to meet that goal during a cruise ship vacation.

"I never thought my weight was an issue, but I'll admit life is a bit different now. For example, I had to buy a pair of pants recently. When I used to shop for larger sizes, the only pants you could find were black and plainly styled. Now I visit the misses' department, and the choices are dizzying—colors and zippers and styles are fun for me, when they never were before. I do keep a rule about clothing, though—I only buy things that I love, and absolutely no stretchy "buffet pants" allowed. Elastic waists let you eat too much—so they are off the menu!

270 Calories

Lentil Soup

—Jenita Terzic, Crestwood, Kentucky

A great source of fiber, this soup is low in calories and high in satisfaction.

Prep time: 15 minutes
Cook time: 40 minutes

- 2 tablespoons olive oil
- 1 large onion, chopped
- 2 large carrots, chopped
- 2 ribs celery, thinly sliced
- 4 cloves garlic, minced
- 1 teaspoon ground sweet paprika
- 1 teaspoon curry powder
- ½ teaspoon ground turmeric
- ½ teaspoon salt
- ½ teaspoon ground black pepper
- 1 bag (16 ounces) lentils, picked over and rinsed
- 8 cups reduced-sodium, fat-free chicken or vegetable broth
- 2 cups water

In a Dutch oven or large saucepan over medium heat, warm the oil. Add the onion, carrots, celery, and garlic. Cook, stirring often, about 8 minutes, or until tender. Stir in the paprika, curry powder, turmeric, salt, and pepper.

Add the lentils, broth, and water. Bring to a boil. Reduce the heat to low, cover, and simmer, stirring occasionally, 25 to 30 minutes, or until the lentils are very tender.

Makes 8 servings

Per serving: *270 calories, 18 g protein, 39 g carbohydrate, 3.5 g fat, 0 mg cholesterol, 630 mg sodium, 17 g fiber*

Diet Exchanges: *0 milk, 1 vegetable, 0 fruit, 0 bread, ½ meat, 1 fat*

2½ Carb Choices

SECRETS OF WEIGHT-LOSS WINNERS

• Eat only when you're hungry, and stop eating when you're no longer hungry. It's very Zen, and much easier said than done.

—Thomas Schoeck, Slingerlands, New York

• Guaranteed to work: Eat less and exercise more. Every 3,500 calories burned and not replaced means the loss of 1 pound.

—John McArthur, Lakeland, Florida

Fall Squash Soup

180 Calories

—Shirley Hill, Chatham, Ontario, Canada

Squash, onion, and apple are roasted, then pureed into a creamy, luscious soup. Look for peeled squash chunks in the market; they make the prep a breeze.

Prep time: 25 minutes
Roast time: 45 minutes

1 large butternut squash, peeled, halved, and seeded, or 9 cups (48 ounces) pre-cut squash

3 medium Mutsu apples or other cooking apples, peeled, cored, and quartered

1 large onion, cut into chunks

3 cloves garlic, peeled

2 tablespoons extra virgin olive oil

½ teaspoon salt

½ teaspoon ground black pepper

6 cups reduced-sodium, fat-free chicken or vegetable broth

Parsley sprigs

Preheat the oven to 400°F. Coat 2 large rimmed baking sheets or a large roasting pan with olive oil spray.

Cut the squash into 1½" chunks. Place the squash, apples, onion, and garlic on the prepared baking sheets or pan. Drizzle with the oil and sprinkle with the salt and pepper. Toss to mix well.

Roast the vegetables and apples, stirring occasionally, 40 to 45 minutes, or until very tender. Remove from the oven and let cool briefly.

In a food processor, in batches if necessary, puree the vegetables until smooth. Add broth as needed to thin the mixture.

Transfer the puree to a large saucepot and stir in the remaining broth. Warm over medium heat, stirring often, until the soup is piping hot. Garnish with parsley.

Makes 6 servings

Per serving: *180 calories, 5 g protein, 32 g carbohydrate, 5 g fat, 0 mg cholesterol, 760 mg sodium, 5 g fiber*

Diet Exchanges: *0 milk, 3½ vegetable, ½ fruit, 0 bread, 0 meat, 1 fat*

2 Carb Choices

Maria's Tortilla Soup

—Mary Fredrickson, Plymouth, Minnesota

"I make this soup often during the winter and have it for lunch and dinner. It's filling and not laden with useless calories."

Prep time: 35 minutes (includes stripping the chicken from the bone and straining the soup)
Cook time: 1½ to 2 hours
Chill time: Up to 24 hours

- 1 chicken (3½ to 4 pounds), rinsed, giblets reserved for another use
- 4 ribs celery with leaves
- 1 large onion, halved
- 12 cups water
- 4 cloves garlic, sliced
- 1 teaspoon salt
- 4 carrots, sliced
- ¼ cup chopped fresh cilantro
- Sliced pickled jalapeño chile peppers (optional)
- Ground black pepper
- 2 cups baked tortilla chips, coarsely crumbled
- 1 cup shredded part-skim mozzarella cheese

Place the chicken in a large saucepot. Add the leaves from the celery. Slice the remaining celery, place in a plastic bag, and refrigerate for later. Cut half the onion into chunks and add to the saucepot. Coarsely chop the remaining onion and refrigerate with the sliced celery.

Add the water, garlic, and salt to the saucepot, and bring to a boil over high heat. Skim off the foam that rises to the surface.

Reduce the heat to medium. Simmer, uncovered, for about 1 hour, or until the chicken is tender when pierced with a fork.

Transfer the chicken to a bowl. Cover loosely with waxed paper, and let stand until cool enough to handle. Remove and discard the skin and bones. Tear the meat into large chunks. Cover and refrigerate if finishing soup the next day.

Strain the broth through a fine strainer into a large measuring cup or bowl. Discard the solids. If possible, refrigerate the broth overnight to harden any fat so it is easily removed. Otherwise, skim off the fat that rises to the surface.

Pour the strained broth into a clean saucepot. Add the reserved sliced celery and chopped onion, the carrots, cilantro, and jalapeño peppers to taste (if desired). Season to taste with salt and black pepper. Bring to a boil over high heat.

Reduce the heat to medium-low and simmer, uncovered, about 30 minutes, or until the vegetables are tender. Stir in the chicken and heat through.

Ladle the soup into 8 wide bowls and top evenly with the chips and mozzarella.

Makes 8 servings

Per serving: *310 calories, 33 g protein, 16 g carbohydrate, 12 g fat, 90 mg cholesterol, 630 mg sodium, 2 g fiber*

Diet Exchanges: *0 milk, 1 vegetable, 0 fruit, 1 bread, 4½ meat, 1½ fat*

1 Carb Choice

Low Fat! Creamy Cauliflower Soup

140 Calories

—Angie Erickson, Wolford, North Dakota

"This soup fills me up, tastes great, and has plenty of vitamins and fiber!"

Prep time: 15 minutes
Cook time: 35 minutes

1 tablespoon canola oil

1 rib celery, sliced

1 small onion, chopped

1 large head cauliflower, separated into small florets

½ cup uncooked rice

2 cans (14½ ounces each) reduced-sodium, fat-free chicken broth

2 cups water

1 cup fat-free milk

1 cup fat-free half-and-half

1 cup reduced-fat shredded Cheddar cheese

Salt

Ground black pepper

In a Dutch oven or large heavy saucepot over medium heat, warm the oil. Add the celery and onion. Cook, stirring often, about 12 minutes, or until tender.

Stir in the cauliflower, rice, broth, and water. Cover and bring to a boil over high heat. Reduce the heat to low and simmer, covered, about 20 minutes, or until the vegetables and rice are tender. Remove ½ to 1 cup florets and set aside.

Puree the soup, in batches if necessary, in a blender or food processor, and return to the pot.

Stir the milk and half-and-half into the soup. Bring just to a simmer over medium-low heat. Remove from the heat, and stir in the reserved cauliflower and the Cheddar. Season to taste with salt and pepper.

Makes 8 servings

Per serving: *140 calories, 9 g protein, 15 g carbohydrate, 6 g fat, 15 mg cholesterol, 570 mg sodium, 2 g fiber*

Diet Exchanges: *0 milk, 1 vegetable, 0 fruit, ½ bread, 1 meat, 1 fat*

1 Carb Choice

100 Calories

Lime and Tortilla Soup

—Nikki Johnson, Fridley, Minnesota

"This is low in calories and surprisingly filling for a broth-based soup. Everyone in the family loves it and it doesn't feel like I deprive myself of flavor."

Prep time: 10 minutes
Bake time: 8 minutes
Cook time: 10 minutes

  2 **whole wheat tortillas (8" in diameter)**
    Coarse salt
  4 **cups reduced-sodium, fat-free chicken broth**
  1 **pound tomatoes, chopped**
  1 **pound (2 cups) chopped, cooked chicken breast**
  ½ **cup chopped fresh cilantro, or to taste**
  3 **or 4 limes**
    Salt
    Ground black pepper

Preheat the oven to 375°F. Stack the tortillas and cut into thin wedges. Spread out on a large baking sheet and coat lightly with olive oil spray. Bake, stirring once, about 8 minutes, or until lightly browned and crispy. Sprinkle lightly with coarse salt.

In a large saucepan over high heat, combine the broth and tomatoes. Cover and bring to a boil. Reduce the heat to medium and simmer, covered, 5 to 7 minutes, or until the tomatoes have softened. Add the chicken and cilantro, and heat through. Remove from the heat and cover to keep warm.

Squeeze ¼ cup juice from 2 or 3 limes. Cut 4 thin slices of the remaining lime. Stir the lime juice into the soup and season to taste with salt and pepper. Ladle soup into 4 bowls and float a slice of lime in each. Serve with the baked tortilla pieces.

Makes 4 servings

Per serving: *100 calories, 5 g protein, 14 g carbohydrate, 1.5 g fat, 0 mg cholesterol, 600 mg sodium, 1 g fiber*

Diet Exchanges: *0 milk, 0 vegetable, 0 fruit, 1 bread, ½ meat, ½ fat*

1 Carb Choice

Black Bean Soup

140 Calories

—Jody Popik, Twinsburg, Ohio

"Here's how I like to serve this: I put ½ cup cooked basmati rice in a wide bowl, ladle some soup over, and top with fat-free sour cream and a sprinkle of grated reduced-fat Cheddar."

Prep time: 10 minutes
Cook time: 40 minutes

- 4 cups reduced-sodium, fat-free chicken broth
- 4 cans (15 ounces each) black beans, rinsed and drained
- 1 can (28 ounces) crushed tomatoes
- 1 large onion, chopped
- 1 to 2 tablespoons ground cumin
- 1 to 2 teaspoons garlic powder
  Salt
  Ground black pepper

In a Dutch oven or large saucepan over medium heat, stir together the broth, black beans, tomatoes, and onion. Stir in the cumin and garlic powder, and season to taste with salt and pepper. Bring to a boil.

Reduce the heat to low, cover, and simmer, stirring occasionally, 30 to 40 minutes, or until the flavors have blended.

Using an immersion blender, or in batches in a food processor, puree the soup.

Makes 10 servings

Per serving: *140 calories, 9 g protein, 27 g carbohydrate, 0.5 g fat, 0 mg cholesterol, 750 mg sodium, 8 g fiber*

Diet Exchanges: *0 milk, 1½ vegetable, 0 fruit, 1½ bread, 0 meat, 0 fat*

2 Carb Choices

It Worked for Me!

Jackie Dornblaser

VITAL STATS

Weight lost: 24 pounds

Time to goal: 1½ years

Amazing results: Meals are light and elegant now—never fried!

Jackie's motivation to pare off the pounds came from a source that is hard to ignore: painfully damaged knee cartilage. Wear and tear had taken its toll, and a fall made things worse, but Jackie's doctor told her she could ease her pain considerably by losing 15 or 20 pounds. That was all she needed to hear to become bound and determined to reach her goal.

"I had always had a bit of a weight issue, but once I was facing damage to my one good knee [the other had already been operated on], I knew I had to focus. My doctor told me that every pound you lose takes 4 pounds of pressure off of your knee joints. The possibility of being able to avoid knee replacement surgery really gave me the incentive to get started. My youngest son was also planning his wedding at that time, and so I gave myself the tall order of losing 20 pounds in 3 months.

I joined a Weight Watchers group that

meets right at my office—it couldn't have been more convenient. It felt like it took a long time to lose the weight. Since hitting my personal goal weight of 150 I have become a "lifetime member" (meaning I weigh in once a month). I'll admit, though, that with menopause and other changes, 5 pounds has crept back on, and it does tend to bother me.

I continue to eat based on the Weight Watchers core program that allows you to focus on fruits, vegetables, and protein without having to count points. I watch my portions and eat until I'm satisfied. I am not a gourmet cook, but this has really changed my eating style: My refrigerator is full of veggies, and I hardly ever cook potatoes or pasta anymore. Dinner used to be made in the frying pan every night—but now I use a slower cooker. And I used to sit down with an entire bag of cookies to snack on. Now I might eat just a half a cookie—I find I really prefer unsalted pretzels!

Low-Calorie "Lunch for the Week"

110 Calories

—Joy Backes, Yardley, Pennsylvania

"This soup packs well, is easily microwaved at work or at home, and is especially tasty seasoned with a teaspoon of Parmesan cheese."

Prep time: 20 minutes
Cook time: 35 minutes

1 tablespoon olive oil

1 large clove garlic, minced

3 small zucchini, halved lengthwise and cut into $\frac{1}{2}$" slices

6 cups reduced-sodium, fat-free chicken or vegetable broth

5 medium carrots, sliced

2 ribs celery, sliced

$\frac{1}{2}$ small head cabbage, cored and coarsely chopped

$\frac{1}{2}$ cup frozen peas, corn, and/or green beans (optional)

In a Dutch oven or large saucepan over medium heat, warm the oil. Add the garlic and cook, stirring, until golden. Add the zucchini and cook, stirring frequently, until lightly browned. Add the broth, carrots, and celery. Bring to a boil, reduce the heat, cover, and simmer 10 minutes. Add the cabbage and frozen vegetables, if desired. Bring to a boil. Cover and simmer about 15 minutes, or until all the vegetables are tender.

Makes 4 servings

Per serving: *110 calories, 4 g protein, 17 g carbohydrate, 4 g fat, 0 mg cholesterol, 840 mg sodium, 6 g fiber*

Diet Exchanges: *0 milk, 3 vegetable, 0 fruit, 0 bread, 0 meat, 1 fat*

1 Carb Choice

Snacks, Sandwiches, Pizzas, and Sides

SNACKS

SANDWICHES

PIZZAS

SIDES

60 Calories

Gingered Salsa

—Margaly Patterson, Miami, Florida

"I am on my weight-loss journey and I've fallen in love with ginger. This salsa is a healthy, low-fat, nutritious dip for low-fat or whole grain chips. It can be eaten with bread or smothered on any meat."

Prep time: 10 minutes
Standing time: 10 minutes

  6 medium tomatoes, chopped
¼ cup chopped scallions
   Juice of 1 lemon
   Juice of ½ lime
  2 tablespoons extra virgin olive oil
  1 tablespoon finely grated fresh ginger
  1 tablespoon chopped fresh flat-leaf parsley
  1 clove garlic, minced
   Salt
   Ground black pepper

In a medium bowl, mix together the tomatoes, scallions, lemon and lime juice, oil, ginger, parsley, and garlic. Season to taste with salt and pepper. Let the salsa stand 10 to 30 minutes before serving.

Makes 8 servings, ½ cup each (4 cups)

Per serving: *60 calories, 1 g protein, 6 g carbohydrate, 4 g fat, 0 mg cholesterol, 5 mg sodium, 2 g fiber*

Diet Exchanges: *0 milk, 1 vegetable, 0 fruit, 0 bread, 0 meat, 1 fat*

½ Carb Choice

It Worked for Me!

Lauren Huff

VITAL STATS

Weight lost: 60 pounds

Time to goal: 1½ years

Amazing results: Becoming a positively healthy role model for her daughters

Like many people, Lauren Huff found her weight slowly becoming a problem over the course of time. A few extra pounds stuck around after high school, and then the "baby fat" gained from pregnancy also became permanent. The day Lauren made the decision to lose weight was a memorable one for her, particularly because she credits her faith in God for sending her that important message.

"It was January 15, 2005, when I heard from God that it was time for me to lose weight. The signs had been there for a while: All of my clothes were getting too tight, and I was already having to shop at Lane Bryant (I couldn't buy things at Target or Wal-Mart anymore). But it wasn't until that particular day that I got the message. The problem was, I really didn't think I could lose weight.

"Despite my doubts, I found a way to keep saying to myself, 'Yes, you can do this.' I started on the South Beach Diet; the first 2-week phase is very extreme. You eat no fruits or breads at all; for me, it was easiest to stick with salad and cheese and eggs.

I expected to see dramatic weight loss immediately. I had read that with South Beach you can drop 10 pounds right away, but that's not what happened for me. I did lose some weight in those first 2 weeks, but it was all I could do to stick with it and keep hoping. And after a while the scale did start moving—albeit very slowly.

I've always loved food, and brownies are a special weakness for me. My connection to food is emotional, and so even though I wasn't hungry on the diet, I would get cravings for a brownie and have to stop myself, say a prayer, and take a drink of water. I think it was the prayers that really got me through!

Soon I saw that my clothes were getting bigger. Once that started happening, I was motivated to keep going. I work in a school, and when fall rolled around, my coworkers were amazed at how I looked. As good as that makes me feel, it's even more important to me that I have energy now to play with my children until they are the ones who poop out first!

90 Calories

Dried Cherry Salsa

—Michele Dipert, Hartwell, Georgia

This is wonderful when served with grilled swordfish or tuna. You might also consider using it as a topping for turkey burgers or chicken breasts.

Prep time: 10 minutes
Microwave time: 1 minute
Chill time: 3 hours

- ½ cup dried cherries
- ½ cup cherry preserves
- 2 tablespoons red wine vinegar
- ½ cup chopped red onion
- ½ cup chopped yellow bell pepper
- 1 to 2 tablespoons chopped, seeded jalapeño chile pepper (wear plastic gloves when handling)
- 1 to 2 tablespoons chopped fresh cilantro
- 1 tablespoon lemon or lime juice

Combine the dried cherries, cherry preserves, and vinegar in a small microwaveable bowl, and stir to mix well. Cover with a lid or vented plastic wrap and microwave on high for 1 to 1½ minutes, or until heated through. Remove from the oven and let stand for 5 minutes.

Stir in the red onion, bell pepper, jalapeño, cilantro, and lemon or lime juice. Refrigerate, covered, for 3 to 4 hours or overnight.

Makes 8 servings, 3 tablespoons each (1½ cups)

Per serving: *90 calories, 1 g protein, 21 g carbohydrate, 0 g fat, 0 mg cholesterol, 0 mg sodium, 1 g fiber*

Diet Exchanges: *0 milk, 0 vegetable, ½ fruit, 1 bread, 0 meat, 0 fat*

1½ Carb Choices

15 Calories

Easy Low-Cal Dressing or Dip

—Morgan Riggan, Nanaimo, British Columbia, Canada

"I use this as a dressing for salads, as a dip for veggies, and in pita pockets. It's so low in calories, but full of flavor."

Prep time: 5 minutes

1 cup salsa (use your favorite)
¼ cup fat-free sour cream
1 tablespoon Dijon mustard
   Salt-free seasoning (optional)

In a medium bowl, stir together the salsa, sour cream, and mustard. If desired, add seasoning to taste.

Makes 10 servings, 2 tablespoons each (1¼ cups)

Per serving: *15 calories, 0 g protein, 3 g carbohydrate, 0 g fat, 0 mg cholesterol, 160 mg sodium, 0 g fiber*

Diet Exchanges: *0 milk, 0 vegetable, 0 fruit, 0 bread, 0 meat, 0 fat*

0 Carb Choices

SHOPPING SAVVY

Spoon Fruits and Fruit Butter

For over 20 years, Justin Rashid's company, American Spoon Foods, has been preserving Northern Michigan's luscious summer-ripe fruit. American Spoon Foods makes jams, sugar-free fruit butters, and sugar-free spreadable fruit—named *spoon fruits* because they're too thick to spread with a knife. *Fruit butter* and *spoon fruit* may not sound like diet food, but they have only 15 to 30 calories per fruity tablespoon, and no fat. In addition, the butters and spoon fruits are sweetened only with fruit juice. Spread cinnamon-spiked Apple Butter on wheat toast or slather Sour Cherry or Blueberry Spoon Fruit on oatmeal pancakes. More info on the web at www.spoon.com or call 888-735-6700 to order.

80 Calories

Cranberry-Almond Jam

—Irene O'Donnell, Moline, Illinois

*"This is an easy, low-calorie spread that is delicious on toast
or a toasted English muffin."*

Prep time: 5 minutes
Microwave time: 12 minutes

  2 cups fresh or frozen cranberries,
    picked over and rinsed
  ⅓ cup apple juice
  1 cup sugar
  ¾ teaspoon ground cinnamon
  1 teaspoon vanilla extract
  ¾ teaspoon almond extract

In a large microwaveable bowl, combine the cranberries and apple juice. Cover lightly with waxed paper or a lid. Microwave on high, stirring several times, about 7 minutes, or until the cranberries soften and burst. Stir in the sugar and cinnamon.

Cover and microwave, stirring once or twice, 5 minutes more, or until slightly thickened. Remove from the oven and let cool. Stir in the vanilla and almond extracts, transfer to a container, cover, and refrigerate until ready to serve.

Makes 12 servings, ¼ cup each (3 cups)

Per serving: *80 calories, 0 g protein, 20 g carbohydrate, 0 g fat, 0 mg cholesterol, 0 mg sodium, 0 g fiber*

Diet Exchanges: *0 milk, 0 vegetable, 0 fruit, 1 bread, 0 meat, 0 fat*

1 Carb Choice

90 Calories

Crispy Sweet Tortilla Chips

—Ginnie Bivona, Dallas, Texas

"This is my low-carb version of Grandmom's pie crust strips. You really can't eat just one!"

Prep time: 5 minutes
Bake time: 8 minutes

> 4 low-carb flour tortillas (10" in diameter)
> 2 tablespoons reduced-calorie, trans-free margarine
> 2 tablespoons Splenda
> Ground cinnamon

Preheat the oven to 400°F. Cover 2 baking sheets with foil.

Spread 1 tortilla with some margarine. Sprinkle generously with Splenda and cinnamon. Stack a tortilla on top of the first and repeat. Repeat two more times, using all the tortillas, margarine, and Splenda. Cut the stack into 6 wedges. Separate the wedges and arrange in single layers on the prepared baking sheets.

Bake for about 8 minutes, or until the chips are lightly brown. These brown quickly, so keep an eye on them. Allow to cool on the foil.

Makes 6 servings, 4 wedges each (24 wedges)

Per serving: *90 calories, 5 g protein, 8 g carbohydrate, 6 g fat, 0 mg cholesterol, 290 mg sodium, 4 g fiber*

Diet Exchanges: *0 milk, 0 vegetable, 0 fruit, 0 bread, 0 meat, 1 fat*

½ **Carb Choice**

Crispy Sweet Tortilla Chips with
Gingered Salsa (page 80)

90 Calories

Crispy Tortilla Chips

—Ginnie Bivona, Dallas, Texas

"These are wonderfully satisfying. They fix my need for something to nibble on that is low-carb. And they're tasty!"

Prep time: 5 minutes
Bake time: 8 minutes

4 low-carb flour tortillas (10" in diameter)
1½ tablespoons extra virgin olive oil
Garlic salt or seasoned salt
1 to 2 tablespoons shredded Parmesan cheese (optional)

Preheat the oven to 400°F. Cover 2 baking sheets with foil.

Brush 1 tortilla with some oil and sprinkle generously with garlic salt or seasoned salt. Stack a tortilla on top of the first and repeat, brushing and seasoning. Repeat two more times, using all the tortillas and oil. Cut the stack into 6 wedges. Separate the wedges and arrange in single layers on the prepared baking sheets.

Bake for about 8 minutes, or until the chips are lightly browned. If you are adding cheese, sprinkle it on wedges just as the edges are barely beginning to brown. These brown quickly, so keep an eye on them. Allow to cool on the foil.

Makes 6 servings, 4 wedges each (24 wedges)

Per serving: *90 calories, 5 g protein, 7 g carbohydrate, 7 g fat, 0 mg cholesterol, 340 mg sodium, 4 g fiber*

Diet Exchanges: *0 milk, 0 vegetable, 0 fruit, 0 bread, 0 meat, 1 fat*

½ **Carb Choice**

Parmesan Pita Chips with Hummus

220 Calories

—Elizabeth Martlock, Jim Thorpe, Pennsylvania

Prep time: 5 minutes
Bake time: 8 minutes

  4 **small whole wheat pitas (6" in diameter), each cut into 6 wedges**
1½ **tablespoons olive oil**
  2 **teaspoons Italian dried herb seasoning**
  ¼ **cup grated Parmesan cheese**
  1 **cup prepared hummus**
     Assorted olives (optional)

Preheat the oven to 350°F. Coat a large baking sheet with olive oil spray.

In a large bowl, combine the pita wedges, oil, and seasoning, and toss to thoroughly coat. Arrange the wedges on the prepared baking sheet and sprinkle with the Parmesan.

Bake until light golden brown, 8 to 12 minutes. Transfer to a shallow bowl and serve warm with the hummus and olives (if desired).

Makes 6 servings, 4 wedges each (24 wedges)

Per serving: *220 calories, 8 g protein, 29 g carbohydrate, 9 g fat, 5 mg cholesterol, 530 mg sodium, 5 g fiber*

Diet Exchanges: *0 milk, 0 vegetable, 0 fruit, 2 bread, 0 meat, 1½ fat*

2 Carb Choices

160 Calories

Grilled Jalapeño-Tuna Bruschetta

—Minerva Daniel, Sacramento, California

"The celery gives this a great crunch that makes me feel like I am biting into something. The bruschetta is the little bit of bread I allow myself to eat and I love this grilled. If you would like it with more bite, you can leave some jalapeño seeds in or add another pepper."

Prep time: 10 minutes
Cook time: 2 minutes

4 tablespoons olive oil

8 slices (½" thick) cracked-wheat country bread, or 16 slices crusty baguette (sliced on the diagonal)

2 cans (6 ounces each) light tuna in water, drained and flaked

1 rib celery, finely chopped

¼ cup chopped red onion

¼ cup chopped fresh cilantro or flat-leaf parsley

1 to 2 tablespoons lemon juice

1 or 2 jalapeño chile peppers, seeded and finely chopped (wear plastic gloves when handling)

Ground black pepper

Coat a barbecue grill or ridged grill pan with olive oil spray and heat to medium-hot. Using 2 tablespoons oil, evenly brush both sides of the bread slices.

Grill the bread, in batches if necessary, until one side has dark grill marks, and then turn them to toast the other side. Transfer to a platter.

In a medium bowl, mix the tuna, celery, red onion, cilantro or parsley, lemon juice, jalapeño pepper, and black pepper to taste. Stir in the remaining 2 tablespoons oil.

Spread the tuna mixture evenly over the toast. If using the country bread, cut each slice in half.

Makes 8 servings

Per serving: *160 calories, 12 g protein, 11 g carbohydrate, 8 g fat, 10 mg cholesterol, 250 mg sodium, 1 g fiber*

Diet Exchanges: *0 milk, 0 vegetable, 0 fruit, 1 bread, 1½ meat, 1½ fat*

1 Carb Choice

Low-Fat Spinach Dip

—Gina Powell, Las Vegas, Nevada

"When I want to indulge in something creamy I make this and I can "pig out" guilt free! This is a satisfying dip for any vegetable or low-fat cracker. You will love it!"

Prep time: 10 minutes
Chill time: 30 minutes

1 cup plain low-fat yogurt

½ cup chopped cooked (or frozen and thawed) spinach, well drained and squeezed dry

½ cup drained canned water chestnuts, chopped

¼ cup chopped sweet white onion

Garlic powder

Salt

Ground black pepper

In a serving dish, stir together the yogurt, spinach, water chestnuts, and onion. Season to taste with garlic powder, salt, and pepper. Cover and refrigerate for at least 30 minutes.

Makes 8 servings (3 cups, or generous ⅓ cup each)

Per serving: *30 calories, 2 g protein, 5 g carbohydrate, 0 g fat, 0 mg cholesterol, 35 mg sodium, 0 g fiber*

Diet Exchanges: *0 milk, ½ vegetable, 0 fruit, 0 bread, 0 meat, 0 fat*

0 Carb Choices

Taco Spread

—Melissa Resnick, Furlong, Pennsylvania

Serve this mildly piquant spread with baked tortilla chips.

Prep time: 10 minutes
Chill time: 1 hour

- 1 container (12 ounces) 1% low-fat cottage cheese
- 1 package (8 ounces) ⅓-less-fat cream cheese, softened
- 1 package (1¼ ounces) lower-salt taco seasoning
- 3 medium tomatoes, finely chopped
- 1 cup shredded lettuce
- 1 cup shredded reduced-fat Cheddar cheese

In a medium bowl, with a wooden spoon, beat together the cottage cheese, cream cheese, and taco seasoning until well blended. Spread in an 8" × 8" baking dish.

Sprinkle with the tomatoes, lettuce, and Cheddar. Cover and refrigerate for 1 hour.

Makes 8 servings

Per serving: *160 calories, 13 g protein, 8 g carbohydrate, 9 g fat, 30 mg cholesterol, 450 mg sodium, 0 g fiber*

Diet Exchanges: *0 milk, ½ vegetable, 0 fruit, 0 bread, 2 meat, 1½ fat*

½ Carb Choice

310 Calories

Egg and Cucumber–Salad Sandwiches

—Maryellen Kerin, Rockaway, New Jersey

"Very light in calories and wholesome."

Prep time: 5 minutes

  3 **hard-cooked eggs, peeled and chopped**
  ½ **cup finely chopped hothouse cucumber**
  2 **tablespoons reduced-fat mayonnaise**
  2 **teaspoons finely chopped onion**
  ¼ **teaspoon dry mustard**
    Salt
    Ground black pepper
  4 **slices whole wheat bread**
  2 **or more slices tomato**
    Colorful mixed baby greens or spinach

In a medium bowl, stir together the egg, cucumber, mayonnaise, onion, and mustard. Season to taste with salt and pepper.

Spread the mixture on 2 of the bread slices. Top with the tomato slices, mixed greens or spinach, and another slice of bread. Cut sandwiches in half at an angle.

Makes 2 servings

Per serving: *310 calories, 15 g protein, 28 g carbohydrate, 15 g fat, 325 mg cholesterol, 470 mg sodium, 4 g fiber*

Diet Exchanges: *0 milk, ½ vegetable, 0 fruit, 2 bread, 1½ meat, 2 fat*

2 Carb Choices

····· SHOPPING SAVVY ············

Super Juice

How do you juice a pomegranate? You don't have to, now that Pom Wonderful 100% Pomegranate Juice is on the scene. This deep purple, slightly tart refresher is found in the refrigerated juice section of most markets, saving you the trouble of squeezing those little kernels. Pomegranates and their juice are a good source of antioxidants, which block the formation of the cell-damaging free radicals that scar arteries, trigger cancerous cell changes, and accelerate aging. So sip your way to good health with Pom: An 8-ounce serving contains 140 calories and has no added sugar.

220 Calories

Amazing Salad Sandwiches

—Armena Marie, Locust Grove, Virginia

"I have lost over 120 pounds, with this salad sandwich (two a day) being a staple."

Prep time: 10 minutes

  2 tablespoons reduced-fat mayonnaise
1½ teaspoons Dijon mustard
  ¼ teaspoon chopped garlic
    Salt
    Ground black pepper
  8 slices whole wheat bread
  4 leaves lettuce or 1 cup mixed salad
    greens
  2 large tomatoes, sliced
  ½ cup drained jarred roasted red
    peppers, sliced
  4 or more slices sweet onion or red onion
    Red wine vinegar

In a cup, mix the mayonnaise, mustard, and garlic, and season to taste with salt and black pepper. Spread over the bread slices. Top 4 slices with the lettuce or salad greens, tomato slices, roasted peppers, and as many slices of onion as you wish. Drizzle the vegetables with vinegar to taste and top with the remaining bread slices.

Makes 4 servings

Per serving: *220 calories, 7 g protein, 37 g carbohydrate, 5 g fat, 1 mg cholesterol, 550 mg sodium, 6 g fiber*

Diet Exchanges: *0 milk, 2 vegetable, 0 fruit, 2 bread, 0 meat, ½ fat*

2½ Carb Choices

Turkey-Lettuce Wraps

—Sandy Umber, Springdale, Arkansas

"This lean wrap tastes great. It's like a chef's salad without all the heavy dressing. You can make it with ham, too."

Prep time: 5 minutes

- 4 large leaves iceberg lettuce
- ½ pound sliced lean deli roast turkey
- 2 tablespoons sweet and spicy mustard
- 1 green bell pepper, cut into thin strips
- ½ cup shredded reduced-fat cheese (any variety)

Lay the lettuce leaves flat on a cutting board. On one half of each, place one-fourth of the turkey. Spread the turkey with the mustard, and top with the bell pepper strips and cheese. Roll up the lettuce leaves to enclose the turkey, bell pepper, and cheese.

Makes 4 servings

Per serving: *130 calories, 15 g protein, 5 g carbohydrate, 6 g fat, 55 mg cholesterol, 610 mg sodium, 0 g fiber*

Diet Exchanges: *0 milk, ½ vegetable, 0 fruit, 0 bread, 2 meat, ½ fat*

0 Carb Choices

SECRETS OF WEIGHT-LOSS WINNERS

• I eat four to five times a day but only small portions. If I go out to eat, I'm sure to bring home more than half of my meal.

—Loretta Exline, Brookings, Oregon

• Start off easy: Just do a 1-mile walk a day, and go on from there.

—Peggy Miller, Crowley, Louisiana

• Eat six small meals throughout the day instead of three big meals. it will keep your metabolism going.

—Debra Wilfert, Dana Point, California

190 *Calories*

Open-Faced Spinach-Bacon Sandwiches

Sherry Waggoner, Oswego, New York

Prep time: 5 minutes
Cook time: 20 minutes

1 teaspoon olive oil
2 slices turkey bacon
1 bag (6 ounces) baby spinach
2 slices whole wheat bread
2 tablespoons garlic and herb cream cheese
2 thick slices tomato

Preheat the oven to 350°F.

In a medium nonstick skillet over medium-high heat, warm the oil. Add the bacon and cook until crisp. Transfer the bacon to a small plate and crumble.

Return the pan to medium heat. Add the spinach and cook, stirring often, until wilted, 3 to 5 minutes.

Spread each slice of bread with 1 table-spoon cream cheese. Top the bread with the spinach, bacon, and a slice of tomato.

Place the sandwiches on a baking sheet and bake for about 10 minutes, or until browned and warmed through.

Makes 2 servings

Per serving: *190 calories, 7 g protein, 22 g carbohydrate, 9 g fat, 30 mg cholesterol, 510 mg sodium, 6 g fiber*

Diet Exchanges: *0 milk, 1½ vegetable, 0 fruit, 1 bread, 0 meat, 1 fat*

1½ Carb Choices

280 Calories

Amy's Apple Sandwiches

—Armena Marie, Locust Grove, Virginia

"I am what I eat—healthy and sweet."

Prep time: 5 minutes
Bake time: 10 minutes

   8 slices whole wheat bread
   2 tablespoons soy mayonnaise or
      reduced-fat mayonnaise
   4 teaspoons Dijon mustard
   8 slices soy cheese (any variety)
   2 juicy Red Delicious apples, halved,
      cored, and thinly sliced
   2 tablespoons chopped walnuts
      (optional)

Preheat the oven to 325°F. Arrange the bread on a baking sheet.

   Spread mayonnaise and mustard on each of the bread slices and top each with a slice of cheese. Arrange the apple slices on top.

   Bake for about 10 minutes, or until the cheese has melted.

   If desired, sprinkle each sandwich with walnuts. Press slices together or serve the sandwiches open-face.

Makes 4 servings

Per serving: *280 calories, 14 g protein, 32 g carbohydrate, 12 g fat, 5 mg cholesterol, 990 mg sodium, 5 g fiber*

Diet Exchanges: *0 milk, 0 vegetable, ½ fruit, 2 bread, 1 meat, 1½ fat*

2 Carb Choices

SHOPPING SAVVY

Smarter Snacking with Soy

When a snack attack arrives, you'll be ready with your portion-controlled pack of Crum Creek Mills organic Brilliantly Blended Soy Nut Mix. It's a crunchy, salty-sweet toss of dry-roasted soybeans, organic chocolate chips, sunflower seeds, pumpkin seeds, and raisins. With 131 calories, 9 grams protein, and 5 grams fiber—and minutes of satisfying munching—you'll truly savor this guilt-free treat. Tuck a pack into your purse or lunchbox. Sold on the web in ten-packs of single servings at www.crumcreek.com, or call 1-888-607-3500.

300 Calories

Tofu-Spinach Wrap

—Maya Nair, Alpharetta, Georgia

"Filling and nutritious—the spices keep me satisfied."

Prep time: 5 minutes
Cook time: 7 minutes

½ teaspoon ground coriander
⅛ teaspoon ground turmeric
⅛ teaspoon crushed red-pepper flakes
¼ teaspoon salt
¼ teaspoon ground black pepper
1 tablespoon water
⅓ cup finely chopped drained firm tofu
1 teaspoon canola oil
2 cups loosely packed spinach, coarsely chopped
1 whole wheat tortilla (8" in diameter)

In a medium bowl, mix the coriander, turmeric, crushed red pepper, salt, and black pepper with the water. Add the tofu and toss to coat with the spice mixture.

In a medium nonstick skillet over medium-high heat, warm the oil. Add the tofu and cook, stirring, for 5 minutes, or until heated and crisp. Add the spinach and stir to mix well. Cook, stirring, until wilted, about 1 minute. Remove from the heat and warm the tortilla by placing it over the spinach mixture for about a minute. Spoon the mixture onto the tortilla and roll up, folding in the sides.

Makes 1 serving

Per serving: *300 calories, 18 g protein, 25 g carbohydrate, 15 g fat, 0 mg cholesterol, 870 mg sodium, 7 g fiber*

Diet Exchanges: *0 milk, ½ vegetable, 0 fruit, ½ bread, 2 meat, 1 fat*

2 Carb Choices

330 Calories

Flatbread Pizzas

—Sandy Umber, Springdale, Arkansas

Prep time: 10 minutes
Bake time: 10 minutes

2 flatbreads (7" in diameter)
¼ cup pizza sauce
½ pound (1 cup) shredded cooked chicken breast
1 small red bell pepper, thinly sliced
1 small green bell pepper, thinly sliced
½ cup sliced white button mushrooms
2 slices sweet red or white onion, coarsely chopped
¼ cup shredded part-skim mozzarella cheese

Preheat the oven to 400°F.

Place the flatbreads on a large baking sheet and spread evenly with the pizza sauce. Top with the chicken, bell peppers, mushrooms, and onion. Sprinkle with the mozzarella. Bake about 10 minutes, or until the vegetables are tender and the cheese is melted and bubbly.

Makes 2 servings

Per serving: *330 calories, 19 g protein, 42 g carbohydrate, 9 g fat, 10 mg cholesterol, 570 mg sodium, 5 g fiber*

Diet Exchanges: *0 milk, 2 vegetable, 0 fruit, 0 bread, ½ meat, 0 fat*

3 Carb Choices

320 Calories

Pita Pocket Pizzas

—Morgan Riggan, Nanaimo, British Columbia, Canada

"If you make smart selections, this recipe can satisfy your craving for pizza without all the added fat and calories that normally accompany it."

Prep time: 10 minutes
Cook time: 10 minutes
Bake time: 8 minutes

  2 small whole wheat pitas (6" in diameter)
  2 teaspoons olive oil
  1 cup sliced white button mushrooms
  1 small onion, chopped
½ cup chopped red or green bell pepper
  1 bag (6 ounces) baby spinach
½ teaspoon dried basil
   Salt
   Ground black pepper
¼ cup low-sodium pizza sauce or salsa
¼ cup crumbled reduced-fat feta cheese
  2 tablespoons sliced ripe olives (optional)

Preheat the oven to 350°F. Place the pitas on a baking sheet; do not open them up.

In a large nonstick skillet over medium heat, warm the oil. Add the mushrooms, onion, and bell pepper, and cook, stirring often, about 8 minutes, or until tender. Add the spinach in batches, stirring until wilted. Season with the basil and salt and pepper to taste.

Spread the pitas with the pizza sauce or salsa and top with the vegetable mixture. Sprinkle evenly with the feta and the olives, if using. Bake about 8 minutes, or until the cheese has warmed and is lightly browned.

Makes 2 servings

Per serving: *320 calories, 13 g protein, 54 g carbohydrate, 8 g fat, 5 mg cholesterol, 780 mg sodium, 11 g fiber*

Diet Exchanges: *0 milk, 3 vegetable, 0 fruit, 2 bread, ½ meat, 1 fat*

3½ Carb Choices

140 Calories

Diet Pizzas

—Cindy Miner, Sioux Falls, South Dakota

"This is a great alternative to regular pizza, and in my opinion it tastes better."

Prep time: 5 minutes
Bake time: 10 minutes

2 slices light whole wheat bread
2 thin slices Muenster cheese
2 tablespoons pizza sauce
  Crushed red-pepper flakes
6 slices turkey pepperoni

Preheat the oven to 350°F. Arrange the bread on a small baking sheet.

On each bread slice, place a slice of cheese. Spread the pizza sauce on top of the cheese, and sprinkle with crushed red pepper to taste. Top with the pepperoni.

Bake for about 10 minutes, or until the cheese has melted and the sauce is bubbly.

Makes 2 servings

Per serving: *140 calories, 11 g protein, 12 g carbohydrate, 6 g fat, 25 mg cholesterol, 440 mg sodium, 4 g fiber*

Diet Exchanges: *0 milk, ½ vegetable, 0 fruit, ½ bread, 1 meat, ½ fat*

1 Carb Choice

SECRETS OF WEIGHT-LOSS WINNERS

• All exercise is good; if you can incorporate an exercise or sport into your normal day (i.e., five days a week if you work), you can easily incorporate it into your life. For example, ride your bicycle to work.
    —Cheryl Anderson, Portland, Oregon

• Make plans to walk with a friend at least three times a week.
    —Carmen Ludwig, New Rockford, North Dakota

• Try pacing while watching television rather than lying on the couch.
    —Heidi Earle, Gaviota, California

Barbecue Chicken Pizzas

—Sherry Waggoner, Oswego, New York

Prep time: 10 minutes
Bake time: 6 minutes

6 ounces boneless, skinless chicken
  breast, grilled

4 tablespoons barbecue sauce

2 whole wheat tortillas (8" in diameter)

½ cup shredded reduced-fat Cheddar
  cheese

¼ cup thinly sliced red onion

¼ cup Mexican-style corn kernels

1 tablespoon chopped fresh cilantro

Preheat the oven to 400°F.

Slice the chicken into thin strips. Toss the chicken with 2 tablespoons barbecue sauce. Spread the remaining 2 tablespoons sauce on the tortillas. Sprinkle the tortillas with the Cheddar, and top with the chicken, red onion, and corn.

Place the tortillas on a baking sheet. Bake pizzas for 6 to 8 minutes, or until warmed through and bubbly. Top with the cilantro.

Makes 2 servings

Per serving: *350 calories, 31 g protein, 45 g carbohydrate, 8 g fat, 70 mg cholesterol, 580 mg sodium, 3 g fiber*

Diet Exchanges: *0 milk, 0 vegetable, 0 fruit, 2½ bread, 4 meat, ½ fat*

3 Carb Choices

230 Calories

Nutty Rice Medley

—Cecilia Haberzettl, Pottstown, Pennsylvania

Prep time: 15 minutes
Cook time: 23 minutes

1 cup + 2 tablespoons water
1 cup apple juice
1 cup uncooked, long-grain rice
2 carrots, chopped
¼ teaspoon salt
1 cup finely chopped, peeled, seeded acorn or butternut squash
⅔ cup drained canned juice-packed pineapple chunks (juice reserved)
¼ cup dark or golden raisins
¼ cup finely chopped walnuts
2 tablespoons frozen orange juice concentrate
1 tablespoon brown sugar
¼ teaspoon ground cinnamon

In a heavy medium saucepan, stir together 1 cup water, the apple juice, rice, carrots, and salt. Bring to a boil over medium-high heat. Reduce the heat to low, cover, and simmer for 15 to 20 minutes, or until the rice is tender and the liquid has been absorbed.

Meanwhile, in a microwaveable container with a lid, combine the squash and remaining 2 tablespoons water. Cover and microwave on high, stirring several times, 3 to 5 minutes, or until tender. Drain.

Stir the pineapple chunks into the rice mixture. Add some of the reserved pineapple juice if the mixture seems dry. Add the raisins, walnuts, orange juice concentrate, brown sugar, and cinnamon. Fold in the squash. Cook over medium-low heat, stirring gently, about 5 minutes, or until heated through.

Makes 6 servings

Per serving: *230 calories, 4 g protein, 46 g carbohydrate, 4 g fat, 0 mg cholesterol, 120 mg sodium, 2 g fiber*

Diet Exchanges: *0 milk, 1 vegetable, 1 fruit, 1½ bread, 0 meat, ½ fat*

3 Carb Choices

60 Calories

Simply Done Veggies

—Ronda Ireland, Arcade, New York

Enjoy this refreshing vegetable dish for lunch, or take it to a picnic.

Prep time: 5 minutes
Cook time: 5 minutes
Chill time: 1 hour

  2 **medium yellow zucchini or summer squash, sliced**
  2 **medium green zucchini, sliced**
  1 **can (14½ ounces) diced tomatoes, drained**
  2 **tablespoons light Italian dressing**
    Salt
    Ground black pepper

Place a steamer basket in a large pot with 2" of water. Bring to a boil over high heat. Place the yellow and green zucchini in the basket, cover, and steam about 5 minutes, or until tender-crisp. Drain and transfer to a bowl. Cover and refrigerate until chilled.

Add the tomatoes and dressing, and season to taste with salt and pepper. Mix gently.

Makes 4 servings

Per serving: *60 calories, 3 g protein, 12 g carbohydrate, 1.5 g fat, 0 mg cholesterol, 200 mg sodium, 4 g fiber*

Diet Exchanges: *0 milk, 2 vegetable, 0 fruit, 0 bread, 0 meat, 0 fat*

1 Carb Choice

130 Calories

Awesome Veggie Medley

—Sherry Conrad, Conway, Arkansas

"This goes over really, really well at potlucks, and everyone is always asking for the recipe."

Prep time: 15 minutes
Bake time: 45 minutes

1 small eggplant, peeled and cut into ½" slices

1 medium sweet white or red onion, halved and cut into ½" slices

1 medium zucchini, cut into ½" slices

1 yellow summer squash, cut into ½" slices

1 bell pepper, any color, cut into ½" strips

¼ pound cremini or baby portobello mushrooms, sliced

3 plum tomatoes, cut crosswise into ½" slices

3 tablespoons olive oil

Salt

Ground black pepper

¼ cup freshly grated Parmesan cheese

Preheat the oven to 400°F. Coat a 9" × 13" baking dish with olive oil spray.

Starting with eggplant and ending with tomatoes, layer the vegetables in the prepared baking dish. Drizzle the oil on top, and season to taste with salt and pepper. Place the dish on a baking sheet.

Bake for 40 minutes. Sprinkle with the Parmesan and bake 5 or 10 minutes more, until the vegetables are very tender.

Makes 6 servings

Per serving: *130 calories, 4 g protein, 12 g carbohydrate, 8 g fat, 5 mg cholesterol, 60 mg sodium, 4 g fiber*

Diet Exchanges: *0 milk, 2 vegetable, 0 fruit, 0 bread, 0 meat, 1½ fat*

1 Carb Choice

It Worked for Me!

Jen Sall

VITAL STATS

Weight lost: 42 pounds

Time to initial goal: 6 months

Greatest challenge: Avoiding sweets, especially when results weren't immediate

Jen Sall was once a hard-bodied, soccer-playing girl. She moved to Boulder, Colorado, for college and became addicted to skiing, rock climbing, and hiking. She even quit her pack-a-day habit to be able to run faster, only to gain 15 pounds in 6 months. And then she put on almost 40 more by eating her way through a miserable relationship.

It had been easy for Jen to ignore the weight gain while running and competing in mountain-bike races, but after a 20-minute jog, she was so wiped out that she'd retreat to the couch for her favorite exercise: power-lifting a bag of Doritos and a pint of ice cream.

At the end of 1999, she forced herself to face the facts: She was fit but fat. Though she loved exercising, she hated dieting. She had convinced herself that she could eat any-thing if she worked out hard and threw in the occasional crash diet.

She began revamping her eating style by eliminating added sugar, but a new fitness trainer explained that if she wanted to really lose weight for good, Jen would have to make more permanent changes. He pushed her to eat five or six small meals a day—rather than three large ones—to curb cravings. The bulk of the minimeals came from what was described as clean ingredients: foods with slow-release carbohydrates, such as brown rice, sweet potatoes, and oatmeal. The carbs fueled her training, the fiber kept her full, and the constant supply of energy revved her metabolism. At each meal, she ate a lean protein, like salmon, egg whites, ground buffalo, or organic chicken, to build muscle, resulting in more calories burned.

Six months later, Jen got her reward. In a dressing room, she realized that for the first time since college, she had choices. Now, 5 years later, she still feels great. She has gone from a size 16 to an 8; lost 42 pounds; and packed on a lot of sleek, toned muscle. Jen's get-fit journey continues—and will for the rest of her life.

100 Calories

Diet Copper Pennies

—Rebecca Squires, St. John's, Newfoundland, Canada

Rebecca enjoys these flavorful carrot "pennies" when she is hungry for a snack and wants to avoid tempting junk foods.

Prep time: 10 minutes
Cook time: 10 minutes
Chill time: 12 hours

  3 **large carrots, sliced**
  2 **medium green bell peppers, thinly sliced**
  2 **medium onions, thinly sliced**
  ½ **(10¾-ounce) can reduced-fat, reduced-sodium tomato soup, undiluted**
  ½ **cup fat-free milk**
  ¼ **cup light Italian dressing**
  1 **tablespoon Worcestershire sauce**
  2 **teaspoons Dijon mustard**
      Ground black pepper

Place a steamer basket in a large pot with 2" of water. Bring to a boil over high heat. Place the carrots, bell peppers, and onions in the basket; cover and steam about 10 minutes, or until crisp-tender. Drain.

In a large bowl, whisk together the tomato soup, milk, dressing, Worcestershire, and mustard, and season to taste with black pepper. Add the vegetables and toss to mix well. Cover and refrigerate at least 12 hours to blend the flavors.

Makes 6 servings

Per serving: *100 calories, 3 g protein, 18 g carbohydrate, 2 g fat, 0 mg cholesterol, 200 mg sodium, 3 g fiber*

Diet Exchanges: *0 milk, 3 vegetable, 0 fruit, 0 bread, 0 meat, ½ fat*

1 Carb Choice

Skillet Sweet Potatoes

—Pamela Lebi, Tucson, Arizona

"These sweet potatoes are so filling, I found that I actually eat less, and I am filled up more quickly."

Prep time: 15 minutes
Cook time: 26 minutes

1 tablespoon olive oil
1 large onion, chopped
2 cloves garlic, minced
1 teaspoon dried rosemary
¼ teaspoon crushed red-pepper flakes
2 medium sweet potatoes (1½ pounds), peeled and cut into ¼"-thick slices
½ cup vegetable broth
    Pinch of salt

In a large, deep nonstick skillet over medium heat, warm the oil. Add the onion and garlic and cook, stirring often, about 6 minutes, or until tender. Stir in the rosemary and crushed red pepper.

Add the sweet potato slices and toss gently to coat with the onion mixture. Add the broth and salt. Bring to a boil. Reduce the heat to medium-low. Cover and simmer, stirring occasionally, about 20 minutes, or until the sweet potatoes are tender when pierced with a fork.

Makes 4 servings

Per serving: *170 calories, 3 g protein, 33 g carbohydrate, 3.5 g fat, 0 mg cholesterol, 230 mg sodium, 5 g fiber*

Diet Exchanges: *0 milk, ½ vegetable, 0 fruit, ½ bread, 0 meat, 1 fat*

2 Carb Choices

230 Calories

Oven-Roasted Sweet Potatoes

—Karen MacKenzie, Kennebunk, Maine

*"This is a very healthy alternative to french fries.
My daughters would trade this for fries any night."*

Prep time: 10 minutes
Bake time: 30 minutes

2 medium sweet potatoes (1½ pounds),
   cut into 1" cubes
1½ tablespoons olive oil
½ teaspoon ground cinnamon
  Salt
  Ground black pepper

Preheat the oven to 425°F. Coat a rimmed baking sheet with olive oil spray.

Arrange the sweet potatoes in a mound on the prepared baking sheet. Toss with the oil and cinnamon, and season to taste with salt and pepper. Spread the potato cubes out on the baking sheet.

Bake, stirring every 10 minutes, for about 30 minutes, or until tender.

Makes 4 servings

Per serving: *230 calories, 3 g protein, 42 g carbohydrate, 5 g fat, 0 mg cholesterol, 60 mg sodium, 5 g fiber*

Diet Exchanges: *0 milk, 0 vegetable, 0 fruit, 2½ bread, 0 meat, 1 fat*

3 Carb Choices

60 Calories

Marinated Asparagus

—Rosanne Dover, Rock Hill, South Carolina

"I eat these alone, as a complement to a meal, or chopped and added to a salad."

Prep time: 10 minutes
Cook time: 5 minutes
Chill time: 1 hour

1 **pound fresh asparagus, trimmed**
3 **tablespoons balsamic vinaigrette**
1 **medium red or green bell pepper, chopped**
3 **scallions, thinly sliced**
 Salt
 Ground black pepper

Place a steamer basket in a large pot with 2" of water. Bring to a boil over high heat. Place the asparagus in the basket, cover, and steam about 5 minutes, or until tender. Drain and transfer to a plate. Let stand until cooled.

Drizzle the asparagus with the vinaigrette, then sprinkle with the bell pepper and scallions. Season to taste with salt and pepper. Cover and marinate in the refrigerator 1 hour.

Makes 4 servings

Per serving: *60 calories, 3 g protein, 8 g carbohydrate, 3 g fat, 0 mg cholesterol, 115 mg sodium, 3 g fiber*

Diet Exchanges: *0 milk, 1½ vegetable, 0 fruit, 0 bread, 0 meat, ½ fat*

½ **Carb Choice**

Prosciutto-Grilled Asparagus

—Elizabeth Martlock, Jim Thorpe, Pennsylvania

Prep time: 5 minutes
Grill time: 8 minutes
Cool time: 10 minutes

24 large asparagus spears, trimmed
 2 tablespoons olive oil
    Salt
    Ground black pepper
12 large, paper-thin slices prosciutto

Coat a ridged grill pan or barbecue grill with olive oil spray and heat to medium. Place asparagus on a plate; drizzle with the oil and season to taste with salt and pepper. Roll in the oil to evenly coat.

Grill the asparagus, turning once or twice, about 5 minutes, or until lightly charred and just tender. Transfer to a plate and let cool.

Cut each slice of prosciutto in half. Roll prosciutto around each asparagus spear.

Makes 6 servings

Per serving: *110 calories, 9 g protein, 3 g carbohydrate, 8 g fat, 20 mg cholesterol, 750 mg sodium, 1 g fiber*

Diet Exchanges: *0 milk, ½ vegetable, 0 fruit, 0 bread, 1 meat, 1 fat*

0 Carb Choices

110 Calories

Green Beans with Roasted Red Peppers

—Audra Hungate, Kearney, Missouri

"I like texture, flavor, and color. This has all three. I can also eat a good-size serving and not feel guilty. Looks great on your plate next to fish or chicken."

Prep time: 10 minutes
Cook time: 13 minutes

  2 **tablespoons olive oil**
  1 **tablespoon minced garlic**
  1 **teaspoon Italian dried herb seasoning**
  1 **pound fresh green beans, trimmed and halved**
¼ **teaspoon salt**
    Ground black pepper
¼ **cup reduced-sodium, fat-free chicken broth**
  2 **jarred roasted red peppers, drained and cut up**

In a large, deep nonstick skillet over medium heat, combine the oil, garlic, and seasoning. Cook, stirring, about 1 minute, or until fragrant. Add the green beans and salt, and season to taste with black pepper. Cook, stirring, for 3 minutes, or until the beans are bright green.

Stir in the broth and bring to a simmer. Cover and cook, stirring once or twice, about 8 minutes, or until the beans are tender. Stir in the roasted peppers, cover, and cook 1 minute, or just until heated through.

Makes 4 servings

Per serving: *110 calories, 3 g protein, 10 g carbohydrate, 7 g fat, 0 mg cholesterol, 480 mg sodium, 3 g fiber*

Diet Exchanges: *0 milk, 2 vegetable, 0 fruit, 0 bread, 0 meat, 1½ fat*

1 Carb Choice

100 Calories

Balsamic Spinach

—Kim Stover, Antioch, California

"I really think that spinach is THE super food."

Prep time: 5 minutes
Cook time: 10 minutes

- 1 **large onion, chopped**
- 8 **ounces white button mushrooms, sliced**
- ½ **teaspoon ground black pepper**
- ¼ **teaspoon salt**
- 1 **bag (20 ounces) baby spinach**
    Pinch of ground red pepper, or to taste
- 2 **to 3 tablespoons good-quality balsamic vinegar**

Coat a large, deep nonstick skillet or Dutch oven with olive oil spray and warm over medium heat. Add the onion and mushrooms, and sprinkle with ¼ teaspoon black pepper and ⅛ teaspoon salt. Cook, stirring often, about 6 minutes, or until the mushrooms are tender and lightly browned.

Add the spinach, in batches, tossing until wilted. Sprinkle with the remaining ¼ teaspoon pepper and ⅛ teaspoon salt and the ground red pepper. Drizzle with the vinegar and stir gently to coat the mixture. Serve immediately.

Makes 4 servings

Per serving: *100 calories, 5 g protein, 24 g carbohydrate, 0 g fat, 0 mg cholesterol, 380 mg sodium, 8 g fiber*

Diet Exchanges: *0 milk, 3½ vegetable, 0 fruit, 0 bread, 0 meat, 0 fat*

2 Carb Choices

50 Calories

Cajun Kale

—Diann Garnett, Bethlehem, Pennsylvania

Prep time: 5 minutes
Cook time: 15 minutes

1 **package (10 ounces) chopped fresh kale**
¼ **cup chopped ham**
½ **cup water**
1 **tablespoon Creole seasoning**
   Lemon juice
   Salt
   Ground black pepper

In a large, deep skillet, combine the kale, ham, and water. Cover and cook over medium heat, stirring occasionally, for 15 minutes, or until the kale is tender. Stir in the Creole seasoning. Season to taste with lemon juice, salt, and pepper.

Makes 4 servings

Per serving: *50 calories, 4 g protein, 7 g carbohydrate, 1 g fat, 5 mg cholesterol, 580 mg sodium, 1 g fiber*

Diet Exchanges: *0 milk, 1½ vegetable, 0 fruit, 0 bread, 0 meat, 0 fat*

½ **Carb Choice**

SECRETS OF WEIGHT-LOSS WINNERS

• I treat my housecleaning as a workout. I turn on the music and go to it, flexing my muscles as I go. It keeps me agile and in shape, and my house looks great!
   —Julie Boudreau, Martinton, Illinois

• Reward yourself for hitting small weight milestones along the way. Create a list of items: Visit a favorite art museum, go to a concert, set aside 1 hour a week to read, get a pedicure, go to a flea market, whatever. Put all of these items on strips of paper and place into a jar. When a 5-pound goal is met, pull out one of the strips and reward yourself.
   —Adene Hostetler, Dublin, Ohio

Main Dishes

TURKEY

BEEF

PORK

Michele's Gourmet Black Beans

—Michele Stelljes, Houston, Texas

"The beans are delicious with or without jasmine rice."

Prep time: 5 minutes
Cook time: 18 minutes

1½ tablespoons olive oil
1 large onion, chopped
2 large cloves garlic, minced
1 tablespoon ground cumin
1 teaspoon dried oregano
1 small jar (4 ounces) finely chopped pimientos
3 cans (15 ounces each) black beans, rinsed and drained
¼ cup sherry wine or rice vinegar
Salt
Ground black pepper
1 cup hot cooked brown jasmine rice (optional)
Salsa and chopped fresh cilantro, for serving

In a large, deep skillet over medium heat, warm the oil. Add the onion and cook, stirring often, about 7 minutes, or until tender. Stir in the garlic, cumin, and oregano. Cook and stir for 30 seconds, or until fragrant.

Add the pimientos and their juice. Cook, stirring, to deglaze the pan. Stir in the beans and the sherry or vinegar. Bring to a boil. Reduce the heat to medium-low, cover, and simmer for 10 minutes to blend the flavors. Season to taste with salt and pepper.

Serve over the rice, if desired, with salsa and lots of fresh cilantro.

Makes 6 servings

Per serving: *200 calories, 12 g protein, 37 g carbohydrate, 2.5 g fat, 0 mg cholesterol, 760 mg sodium, 13 g fiber*

Diet Exchanges: *0 milk, 1 vegetable, 0 fruit, 2 bread, 0 meat, ½ fat*

2½ Carb Choices

Santa Fe Homestyle Rice and Beans

—Lori Slone, Chaplin, Connecticut

"This dish is very filling, healthy, and for me, a great comfort food. I enjoy it with a nice light salad—and it helps me to stay full for a long time."

Prep time: 25 minutes (including cooking rice mix)
Microwave time: 8 minutes

  1 box (7 ounces) black beans and rice mix, cooked according to package directions

  1 can (15 ounces) red kidney beans, rinsed and drained

  1 cup corn kernels

  1 small can (4¼ ounces) sliced jalapeño chile peppers, drained

  ½ cup nonfat sour cream

  ½ cup shredded reduced-fat Cheddar or Colby cheese

In a microwaveable dish, stir together the cooked rice mix, kidney beans, corn, and jalapeños. Cover with a lid or waxed paper and microwave on high 5 to 7 minutes, or until heated through. Sprinkle with the cheese, and microwave uncovered for 1 minute longer, or until the cheese is bubbling. Dollop with sour cream, and serve.

Makes 8 servings

Per serving: *170 calories, 8 g protein, 31 g carbohydrate, 1½ g fat, 5 mg cholesterol, 910 mg sodium, 6 g fiber*

Diet Exchanges: *0 milk, 0 vegetable, 0 fruit, ½ bread, ½ meat, 0 fat*

2 Carb Choices

···· SHOPPING SAVVY ····

They're French

Steamed Lentils are a great time-saver from Melissa's, those clever produce people. Precooked to perfection and all natural, they come in a vacuum-sealed bag. Heat (in the bag) and eat, or enjoy cold in a salad. We like to toss them with whole wheat orzo and a dash of olive oil, but they are also super as a side dish, maybe warmed up with a touch of curry powder. These small, nutty-flavored French lentils keep their shape when cooked, and they can help you keep your shape, too. Fiber is a big gun in the diet arsenal and these lentils pack a whopping 16 grams per cup. Look in the refrigerated section of the produce aisle of your favorite supermarket. For more information, go to www.melissas.com.

240 Calories

Chile-Corn Casserole

—Ann Rhew, Floresville, Texas

"Everyone wants the recipe for this tasty dish."

Prep time: 5 minutes
Bake time: 35 minutes

1 package (8 ounces) corn muffin mix
2 cans (15¼ ounces each) cream-style corn
1 cup plain fat-free yogurt
1 can (4½ ounces) chopped mild green chiles, drained
¼ cup chopped red bell pepper
3 scallions, thinly sliced
1 large egg
2 tablespoons snipped fresh dill

Preheat the oven to 350°F. Coat a 9" or 10" cast-iron skillet or 11" × 8" baking pan with cooking spray.

In a large bowl, combine the corn muffin mix, cream-style corn, yogurt, chiles, bell pepper, scallions, egg, and dill. Stir well with a wooden spoon until blended. Transfer the batter to the prepared skillet or pan.

Bake for 35 to 40 minutes, or until firm to the touch, lightly browned, and a wooden pick inserted into the center comes out clean. Cool for a few minutes before serving.

Makes 8 servings

Per serving: *240 calories, 6 g protein, 44 g carbohydrate, 5 g fat, 30 mg cholesterol, 910 mg sodium, 3 g fiber*

Diet Exchanges: *0 milk, ½ vegetable, 0 fruit, 2½ bread, 0 meat, ½ fat*

3 Carb Choices

380 Calories

Southwestern Steam

—Andrew Dunn, Mountain Home, Indiana

This is a great dish to bring to potluck suppers.

Prep time: 10 minutes
Cook time: 25 minutes
Bake time: 10 minutes

2 medium yellow summer squash, sliced (about 5 cups)

2 medium zucchini, sliced (about 5 cups)

1 can (14 to 19 ounces) red beans or kidney beans, rinsed and drained

1 bag (16 ounces) frozen corn kernels

1 bag (16 ounces) frozen baby lima beans

1 can (8 ounces) sliced bamboo shoots, drained

1 can (5 ounces) sliced water chestnuts, drained

¼ cup water

½ teaspoon ground cumin

Salt

Ground black pepper

1 cup reduced-fat shredded Monterey Jack cheese

½ cup chopped fresh cilantro

Preheat the oven to 350°F.

In a large, deep skillet or Dutch oven, combine the squash, zucchini, red or kidney beans, corn, lima beans, bamboo shoots, water chestnuts, and water. Cover and bring to a boil over medium-high heat. Reduce the heat to medium and cook, covered, stirring occasionally, for about 15 minutes, or until the squash and zucchini are tender and the frozen vegetables are warmed through. Drain. Stir in the cumin and season to taste with salt and pepper.

Transfer the vegetable mixture to a large, shallow casserole dish and top with the cheese. Bake for 10 minutes, or until the cheese has melted. Sprinkle with the cilantro before serving.

Makes 8 servings

Per serving: *380 calories, 23 g protein, 66 g carbohydrate, 4.5 g fat, 10 mg cholesterol, 170 mg sodium, 15 g fiber*

Diet Exchanges: *0 milk, 1 vegetable, 0 fruit, 4 bread, 1 meat, ½ fat*

4 Carb Choices

It Worked for Me!

Kim Bensen, 45

VITAL STATS

Weight lost: 213 pounds

Time to goal: 2 years

Greatest challenge: Finding healthy alternatives to old favorite recipes

Kim Bensen, author and mother of four, used to have a tough time shopping for clothes. She could barely squeeze into size 32 pants, and at 5-foot-5½ and 347 pounds, "there wasn't a single day my weight wasn't on my mind," says the Huntington, Connecticut, resident.

Her size caused severe back and knee pain; she had trouble walking, sleeping, and breathing; and her cholesterol was through the roof. Her doctor couldn't even weigh her; his scale didn't go above 300 pounds. He'd simply mark her as OTC—"off the charts."

Kim has always loved food, but thanks to her youthful metabolism and a life filled with physical activities like softball, her weight didn't become an issue until she went off to college, stopped exercising regularly, and started making all her own food choices. "It was junk all the time," she remembers. Instead of the usual freshman 15, Kim struggled with 4 years of 15- to 40-pound weight shifts.

Things got worse when she married, shortly after graduation. Kim quickly broke the 200-pound mark but not without a fight: "I tried everything to lose weight—over-the-counter pills, fad diets, even those shakes Oprah lost a ton with." Though Kim could stick to a regimen to drop as much as 70 pounds, she'd always gain more back than she lost.

The moment that changed everything came in 2001, when Kim was at her heaviest. Her husband Mark, an insulin-dependent diabetic since childhood, contracted an infection that nearly killed him. Surgery saved his life, but the experience shook Kim. "Mark took such good care of himself." Having him so sick finally made her realize that she should be doing the same.

She made diet versions of her favorite recipes, and all the while Mark helped her dodge temptation.

By October 2003, Kim reached her goal: 134 pounds, which she has maintained ever since. "My feet even shrunk a size and a half," she laughs.

Now Kim is a Weight Watchers leader and has self-published a book filled with her own healthy recipes. "I couldn't have done any of this without Mark," she says. "He's taught me that having unconditional support can truly make a difference."

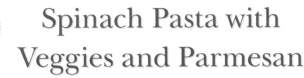

330 Calories

Spinach Pasta with Veggies and Parmesan

—Alicia Auerbach, Grapevine, Texas

This delicious meal tastes great either hot or cold!

Prep time: 10 minutes
Cook time: 22 minutes

½ **pound spinach pasta twists**
2 **tablespoons olive oil**
6 **cloves garlic, thinly sliced**
½ **teaspoon dried basil or Italian seasoning**
1 **bunch broccoli, cut into florets**
1 **cup grape tomatoes, halved**
  Salt
  Ground black pepper
½ **cup shaved Parmesan cheese**

Cook the pasta according to the package directions. Scoop out ½ cup of the pasta-cooking water and reserve. Drain the pasta and return to the cooking pot to keep warm.

Meanwhile, in a large nonstick skillet over medium-high heat, warm the oil. Add the garlic and basil or Italian seasoning. Cook, stirring, about 1 minute, or until the garlic is just starting to turn golden. Add the broccoli. Cover and cook, stirring several times, for 5 minutes. Add the grape tomatoes and cook, stirring once, about 5 minutes longer, or until the broccoli is crisp-tender. If the mixture becomes dry, add up to 3 tablespoons water.

Add the vegetable mixture to the pasta, and season to taste with salt and pepper. Toss well, adding pasta water to moisten, if necessary. Top with the shaved Parmesan before serving.

Makes 4 servings

Per serving: *330 calories, 14 g protein, 47 g carbohydrate, 11 g fat, 5 mg cholesterol, 210 mg sodium, 5 g fiber*

Diet Exchanges: *0 milk, 1 vegetable, 0 fruit, 2½ bread, ½ meat, 1½ fat*

3 Carb Choices

400 Calories

Pasta Primavera

—Leana Faneuf, Treasure Island, Florida

The variety of veggies in this meal makes a colorful and healthy combination that is sure to satisfy.

Prep time: 15 minutes
Cook time: 16 minutes

- 2 cups small broccoli florets
- 2 cups small cauliflower florets
- 2 cups cut green beans
- 1 cup baby carrots, cut into thirds
- 3 tablespoons olive oil
- 1 zucchini, halved lengthwise, then cut into thin slices
- 1 medium red bell pepper, thinly sliced
- ½ teaspoon crushed red-pepper flakes
- ½ pound whole wheat angel hair pasta
  Salt
  Ground black pepper
- ½ cup grated Parmesan cheese

Place a steamer basket in a large pot with 2" of water. Bring to a boil over high heat. Place the broccoli, cauliflower, green beans, and carrots in the basket. Cover and steam for 10 to 12 minutes, or until tender. Drain.

Meanwhile, in a large nonstick skillet over medium heat, warm the oil. Add the zucchini, bell pepper, and crushed red pepper. Cook, stirring often, 6 to 8 minutes, or until tender. Stir in the steamed vegetables, remove from the heat, and cover to keep warm.

Meanwhile, cook the pasta according to package directions. Scoop out and reserve ½ cup pasta-cooking water. Drain the pasta and add to the vegetables. Season to taste with salt and black pepper. Toss, adding pasta water to moisten, if necessary. Sprinkle with the Parmesan.

Makes 4 servings

Per serving: *400 calories, 16 g protein, 55 g carbohydrate, 14 g fat, 10 mg cholesterol, 190 mg sodium, 14 g fiber*

Diet Exchanges: *0 milk, 2½ vegetable, 0 fruit, 0 bread, ½ meat, 2½ fat*

4 Carb Choices

490 Calories

Whole Wheat Linguine with Creamy Tomato-Pesto Sauce

—Elizabeth Martlock, Jim Thorpe, Pennsylvania

Buttery-flavored pine nuts add an unexpected and pleasant crunch to this rich-tasting—but low-fat—pasta.

Prep time: 10 minutes
Cook time: 16 minutes

1 **cup sun-dried tomatoes (not packed in oil)**
¼ **cup grated Parmesan cheese**
2 **tablespoons extra virgin olive oil**
2 **cloves garlic, peeled**
1 **cup fat-free half-and-half**
1 **tablespoon cornstarch**
  Salt
  Ground black pepper
¾ **pound whole wheat linguine**
2 **tablespoons pine nuts, toasted**

In a small bowl, soak the sun-dried tomatoes in boiling water to cover for 10 minutes. Drain, reserving the tomato-soaking water.

In a blender or food processor, combine the sun-dried tomatoes, Parmesan, oil, and garlic; process to a chunky puree. (Add some of the tomato-soaking water to loosen the mixture if necessary.)

In a heavy medium saucepan, whisk the half-and-half and cornstarch until smooth. Bring to a boil over medium heat, stirring until thickened, about 5 minutes. Remove from the heat and stir in the tomato mixture. Season to taste with salt and pepper. Cover to keep warm.

Meanwhile, cook the pasta according to the package directions. Scoop out about ½ cup pasta-cooking water and reserve. Drain the pasta and return it to the cooking pot.

Add the sauce to the pasta and toss, adding pasta water to moisten, if necessary. Sprinkle with the pine nuts.

Makes 4 servings

Per serving: *490 calories, 19 g protein, 80 g carbohydrate, 14 g fat, 5 mg cholesterol, 450 mg sodium, 9 g fiber*

Diet Exchanges: *0 milk, 1½ vegetable, 0 fruit, 0 bread, ½ meat, 2½ fat*

5½ Carb Choices

340 Calories

Spicy Olive Pasta

—Melinda Li, Washington, D.C.

"This recipe cooks in the time it takes for me to order out for pizza—but is so much healthier. The rich flavors are very satisfying."

Prep time: 10 minutes
Cook time: 11 minutes

- 2 tablespoons olive oil
- 2 cloves garlic, minced
- ½ teaspoon crushed red-pepper flakes
- ½ teaspoon ground chipotle chiles
- ½ cup pitted green olives, roughly chopped
- 1 can (14½ ounces) diced tomatoes
  Salt
- ½ pound medium shell pasta
- ⅓ cup chopped fresh basil
- ¼ cup chopped fresh flat-leaf parsley
- 1 tablespoon lemon juice

In a large, heavy skillet over medium heat, warm the oil. Add the garlic, crushed red pepper, and chipotle chiles. Cook, stirring, for 30 seconds, or until fragrant. Stir in the olives and tomatoes (with their juice). Bring to a boil. Reduce the heat and simmer, uncovered, for about 10 minutes, or until lightly thickened. Season to taste with salt.

Meanwhile, cook the pasta according to the package directions. Drain and transfer to the skillet. Add the basil, parsley, and lemon juice, and toss to mix well.

Makes 4 servings

Per serving: *340 calories, 9 g protein, 50 g carbohydrate, 12 g fat, 0 mg cholesterol, 580 mg sodium, 5 g fiber*

Diet Exchanges: *0 milk, 1 vegetable, 0 fruit, 3 bread, 0 meat, 2 fat*

3 Carb Choices

SHOPPING SAVVY

It's Organic

Heinz Tomato Ketchup has been around since 1876. How do they improve upon tradition? By going organic. The same tasty blend of tomatoes and spices now has a "natural" version made with organically grown tomatoes and organic sugar, not high fructose corn syrup. Heinz Organic Ketchup contains 2.5 grams of lycopene per tablespoon; lycopene is a powerful antioxidant that may help to fight disease. Since it is best absorbed with a little fat, enjoy Heinz Organic Ketchup on oven fries, grilled reduced-fat chicken sausages, or turkey burgers. Sold in the natural foods sections of better supermarkets and at club stores.

360 Calories

Light and Creamy Fettuccine with Asparagus

—Lyn King, Leavenworth, Kansas

"I love blue cheese but hate the calories of heavy, fat-laden sauces. This pasta satisfies my craving for a rich blue cheese sauce without adding it to my hips!"

Prep time: 15 minutes
Cook time: 10 minutes

½ **pound fettuccine**
1 **pound asparagus, trimmed and diagonally sliced**
2 **teaspoons trans-free margarine**
4 **medium cloves garlic, minced**
1 **tablespoon all-purpose flour**
1¼ **cups fat-free milk**
¼ **cup reduced-fat cream cheese**
⅓ **cup crumbled Gorgonzola cheese**
   Salt
   Coarsely ground black pepper
2 **tablespoons chopped toasted walnuts**

Bring a large pot of water to a boil over high heat. Add the fettuccine and cook for 6 minutes, stirring often. Stir in the asparagus, and cook 4 to 6 minutes more, or until the fettuccine is al dente and asparagus crisp-tender. Scoop out ½ cup pasta-cooking water and reserve. Drain the pasta and asparagus and return to the cooking pot; cover to keep warm.

Meanwhile, in a medium nonstick saucepan over medium heat, melt the margarine. Add the garlic and cook, stirring, 30 seconds, or until fragrant. Add the flour and cook, stirring, 30 seconds. Gradually add the milk, whisking until smooth. Bring to a boil. Reduce the heat and simmer, stirring often, about 5 minutes, or until thickened and smooth. Remove from the heat.

Whisk in the cream cheese and Gorgonzola until smooth and blended. Season to taste with salt and pepper. Add the sauce to the pasta and toss, adding pasta water to moisten, if necessary. Sprinkle with the walnuts.

Makes 4 servings

Per serving: *360 calories, 17 g protein, 54 g carbohydrate, 9 g fat, 15 mg cholesterol, 240 mg sodium, 5 g fiber*

Diet Exchanges: *½ milk, 1 vegetable, 0 fruit, 3 bread, ½ meat, 1½ fat*

3½ Carb Choices

280 Calories

Grilled Eggplant Parmesan

—Renee Rewiski, Hawthorne, New Jersey

Renee makes a chunky tomato sauce with her homegrown plum tomatoes, and she says the fresh taste of the tomatoes really adds to the flavor of this dish. Toss any leftover sauce with penne or pasta shells and a bit of reduced-fat ricotta cheese for a quick weeknight supper.

Prep time: 20 minutes
Cook time: 45 minutes (for sauce) and
                38 minutes (for eggplant)
Grill time: 8 minutes
Bake time: 30 minutes

T O M A T O S A U C E

- 2 teaspoons olive oil
- 1 large onion, chopped
- 3 cloves garlic, minced
- 4 pounds plum tomatoes, peeled (see Kitchen Tip) and cut into chunks
- ½ cup chopped fresh basil
- ½ teaspoon salt

E G G P L A N T

- 2 medium eggplants, peeled and cut crosswise into ½"-thick slices
- 2 tablespoons olive oil
- 2 teaspoons Italian dried herb seasoning
  Salt
  Ground black pepper
- 1 cup shredded part-skim mozzarella cheese
- 4 tablespoons grated Parmesan cheese

To make the sauce: In a large, heavy saucepan, warm the oil over medium-high heat. Add the onion and garlic and cook, stirring, for about 4 minutes, or until tender. Reduce the heat to low. Add the tomatoes, stirring and breaking them up as they soften. Cook for about 45 minutes, or until thickened. Stir in the basil and salt.

To make the eggplant: Coat a barbecue grill or ridged grill pan with olive oil spray and heat to medium-hot. Brush the eggplant slices with the oil, sprinkle with the Italian seasoning, and season to taste with salt and pepper.

Grill the eggplant, in batches if necessary, turning once, about 8 minutes, or until tender and lightly browned.

Preheat the oven to 350°F. Arrange about 8 eggplant slices in a 13" × 9" baking dish. Sprinkle with ⅓ cup mozzarella and 1 tablespoon Parmesan. Spoon over ⅔ cup sauce, and top with another layer of eggplant and ⅓ cup mozzarella. Add ⅔ cup sauce and the remaining eggplant and mozzarella. Top with ⅔ cup more sauce, and sprinkle with the remaining 3 tablespoons Parmesan. (Reserve any remaining sauce for another use.)

Cover the dish with foil and bake for 20 minutes, or until bubbly and heated through. Uncover and bake 10 minutes longer, or until lightly browned on top.

Makes 4 servings

Per serving: *280 calories, 13 g protein, 27 g carbohydrate, 15 g fat, 20 mg cholesterol, 540 mg sodium, 11 g fiber*

Diet Exchanges: *0 milk, 5 vegetable, 0 fruit, 0 bread, 1½ meat, 2 fat*

2 Carb Choices

— *Kitchen Tip* —

To peel tomatoes, plunge them one at a time into a saucepan of boiling water, and cook for about 30 seconds. Remove with a slotted spoon and place in a bowl of ice water. When cool, the skins will slip off easily.

250 Calories

Tofu Curry

—Vaishali Ramjee, Winter Garden, Florida

"I like to make homemade whole wheat chapatis to enjoy with this dish. This curry is light—I have noticed that eating this dish (and similar dishes) has helped me lose weight . . . which I am still in the process of doing."

Prep time: 15 minutes
Cook time: 20 minutes

  2 **tablespoons olive oil**
  1 **package (8 ounces) firm tofu, drained and cut into bite-size pieces**
  2 **whole cloves**
  2 **whole black peppercorns**
 ½ **stick cinnamon**
  3 **large cloves garlic, minced**
 1" **piece fresh ginger, peeled and grated**
  1 **medium onion, finely chopped**
  1 **large tomato, chopped**
  1 **teaspoon ground turmeric**
  1 **teaspoon garam masala (available in Indian groceries and larger supermarkets)**
 ⅛ **teaspoon ground red pepper, or more to taste**
     Salt
  1 **package (10 ounces) frozen peas**
 ¾ **cup plain fat-free yogurt**
  1 **tablespoon cornstarch**
  2 **tablespoons chopped fresh cilantro (optional)**

In a large nonstick skillet over medium-high heat, warm 1 tablespoon oil. Add the tofu and cook, turning often, about 6 minutes, or until lightly browned. Transfer the tofu to a plate and cover to keep warm.

In the same skillet, over medium heat, warm the remaining 1 tablespoon oil. Add the cloves, peppercorns, and cinnamon stick and cook, stirring, 30 seconds. Add the garlic and ginger, and cook, stirring, about 30 seconds, or until fragrant.

Add the onion and cook, stirring often, about 5 minutes, or until tender. Stir in the tomato and then the turmeric, garam masala, and ground red pepper. Season to taste with salt. Cook, stirring, 3 minutes. Add the peas; reduce the heat, cover, and simmer about 5 minutes, or until heated through.

Whisk together the yogurt and cornstarch, and stir into the curry. Bring to a simmer, stirring. Stir in the tofu and cilantro (if using), and serve immediately.

Makes 4 servings

Per serving: *250 calories, 16 g protein, 24 g carbohydrate, 12 g fat, 0 mg cholesterol, 95 mg sodium, 7 g fiber*

Diet Exchanges: *½ milk, 1 vegetable, 0 fruit, 1 bread, 1½ meat, 1½ fat*

1½ Carb Choices

230 Calories

Squash à la Jacques

—Monica Ball, Norman, Texas

*"This is a warm and zesty meal that leaves me satisfied but not feeling heavy.
Serve with whole wheat bread and a scoop of fat-free yogurt."*

Prep time: 10 minutes
Microwave time: 10 minutes
Stand time: 10 minutes
Cook time: 35 minutes

- 1 medium spaghetti squash
- 1 cup brown lentils, picked over and rinsed
- 4 cups water
- 2 cans (8 ounces each) tomato sauce
- 2 tablespoons minced garlic
- 2 low-sodium vegetable bouillon cubes
- Pinch of ground red pepper
- Salt

Pierce the squash several times with a fork. Place in a large microwaveable baking dish and microwave on high, turning the squash over once, for 15 to 25 minutes, or until fork-tender. Let stand for 10 minutes.

Meanwhile, in a large saucepan or Dutch oven, combine the lentils, water, tomato sauce, garlic, and bouillon cubes. Cover and bring to a boil over high heat. Reduce the heat to medium-low and simmer, covered, stirring occasionally, for about 25 minutes, or until the lentils are tender.

Halve the squash lengthwise. Scoop out and discard the seeds. With a fork, scrape across the squash to form spaghetti-like threads. Add to the lentils, and season with the ground red pepper and salt to taste. Bring to a simmer over medium heat.

Reduce the heat, and cook, uncovered, stirring occasionally, for about 10 minutes more, or until the mixture has thickened and the flavors have blended.

Makes 4 servings

Per serving: *230 calories, 11 g protein, 46 g carbohydrate, 1.5 g fat, 0 mg cholesterol, 650 mg sodium, 11 g fiber*

Diet Exchanges: *0 milk, 4 vegetable, 0 fruit, 0 bread, 0 meat, 0 fat*

3 Carb Choices

410 Calories

Sauté of Shrimp and Veggies in Balsamic Vinegar

—Kathy Gruhn, New York, New York

"Balsamic vinegar adds wonderful flavor and aroma to this dish. As it cooks, it will cook down and slightly thicken, and the taste of the vinegar will go from tangy to a more subtle sweetness. You can use pork medallions or chicken breasts instead of shrimp. To make a vegetarian dish, try firm tofu."

Prep time: 10 minutes
Marinate time: 30 minutes
Cook time: 8 minutes

1½ pounds shrimp (thawed, if frozen), peeled, deveined, and rinsed
½ cup balsamic vinegar
1 bunch broccoli
1 pound shiitake mushrooms
1 tablespoon olive oil
   Salt
   Ground black pepper
2 cups hot cooked brown rice

In a medium bowl, toss the shrimp and ¼ cup balsamic vinegar. Marinate in the refrigerator for 30 minutes.

Meanwhile, cut the broccoli into small florets, keeping ½" of the stalk. Remove and discard the stems of the mushrooms. Thickly slice any large caps.

In a large skillet over medium-high heat, warm the oil. Add the broccoli and cook, stirring, for 2 to 3 minutes, or until nearly fork-tender. Add the mushrooms and cook, stirring, for 2 minutes, or until tender and lightly browned. Season to taste with salt and pepper.

Reduce the heat to medium; add the drained shrimp. Cook, stirring, for 2 minutes. Stir in the remaining ¼ cup balsamic vinegar. Cook, stirring, about 1 minute longer, or until the shrimp are pink and opaque in the thickest part. Serve over the brown rice.

Makes 4 servings

Per serving: *410 calories, 35 g protein, 54 g carbohydrate, 7 g fat, 215 mg cholesterol, 240 mg sodium, 6 g fiber*

Diet Exchanges: *0 milk, 4 vegetable, 0 fruit, 2 bread, 4 meat, 1 fat*

3½ Carb Choices

Shrimp, Mushroom, and Asparagus Stir-Fry

200 Calories

—Melissa Bleier, East Haven, Connecticut

"You can serve this over rice or pasta. I've lost about 40 pounds so far in 9 months."

Prep time: 10 minutes
Cook time: 10 minutes

- 2 tablespoons olive oil
- 2 large portobello mushrooms, sliced, slices cut in half
- 1 pound large shrimp (thawed, if frozen), peeled, deveined, and rinsed
- 1 pound asparagus, trimmed and cut into 1" pieces
- Salt
- Ground black pepper
- Lemon or lime wedges, for serving

In a large, deep nonstick skillet over medium-high heat, warm the oil. Add the mushrooms and cook, stirring often, about 5 minutes, or until tender and lightly browned.

Add the shrimp. Cook, stirring, 1 minute. Add the asparagus and season to taste with salt and pepper. Continue to cook, stirring often, about 4 minutes, or until the shrimp are pink and opaque in the thickest part, and the asparagus is crisp-tender. Serve with the lemon or lime wedges.

Makes 4 servings

Per serving: *200 calories, 24 g protein, 6 g carbohydrate, 9 g fat, 160 mg cholesterol, 160 mg sodium, 2 g fiber*

Diet Exchanges: *0 milk, 1 vegetable, 0 fruit, 0 bread, 3 meat, 1½ fat*

½ **Carb Choice**

480 Calories

Broiled Shrimp Scampi

—Lynne Pizette, Hopkinton, Massachusetts

This is a great party dish, and it's very easy if you buy shrimp that have already been peeled.

Prep time: 15 minutes
Cook time: 10 minutes
Broil time: 5 minutes

- ¾ **pound angel hair pasta**
- 1 **bunch broccoli, cut into small florets**
- ¼ **cup extra virgin olive oil**
- 2 **tablespoons minced garlic**
- ¼ **cup chopped fresh flat-leaf parsley**
- ⅓ **cup dry vermouth or white wine**
- 1 **teaspoon dried basil**
- 2 **tablespoons lemon juice**
- ½ **teaspoon salt**
- ½ **teaspoon ground black pepper**
- 2 **pounds medium shrimp (thawed, if frozen), peeled, deveined, and rinsed**
- ⅓ **cup plain dry bread crumbs**
   Grated Parmesan cheese (optional)

Bring a large pot of salted water to a boil over high heat. Preheat the broiler.

When the water boils, add the pasta. Stir and add the broccoli florets. Cook, stirring frequently, about 4 minutes, or until the pasta is al dente and the broccoli tender. Scoop out ½ cup of the pasta-cooking water and reserve. Drain the pasta and the broccoli. Return to the cooking pot, and cover to keep warm.

Meanwhile, in a large skillet over medium-high heat, warm the oil. Add the garlic and cook, stirring, about 2 minutes, or until fragrant. Stir in the parsley, vermouth or white wine, and basil. Cook, stirring, 1 minute. Stir in the lemon juice, salt, pepper, and reserved pasta water. Cover and reduce the heat; simmer 2 minutes longer.

Place the shrimp in a mound on a large rimmed baking sheet. Spoon about one-half of the garlic-vermouth mixture over the shrimp and toss to coat. Spread the shrimp out in a single layer and sprinkle with the bread crumbs.

Broil the shrimp 4" to 6" from the heat for 3 to 5 minutes, or until the crumbs are browned and the shrimp are pink and opaque in the thickest part.

Stir the remaining garlic mixture into the pasta and broccoli, and transfer to a serving bowl. Arrange the shrimp on top, drizzle with any juices, and toss. Serve immediately with grated Parmesan, if you like.

Makes 6 servings

Per serving: *480 calories, 37 g protein, 51 g carbohydrate, 13 g fat, 200 mg cholesterol, 460 mg sodium, 3 g fiber*

Diet Exchanges: *0 milk, ½ vegetable, 0 fruit, 2½ bread, 4 meat, 2 fat*

3½ Carb Choices

370 Calories

Southwestern Shrimp and Rice Skillet

—Stephanie Little, Cypress, Texas

"This is a satisfying recipe that will help you fill up without overeating. It tastes great and is nutritious."

Prep time: 5 minutes
Cook time: 9 minutes

1½ tablespoons olive oil

  3 to 5 cloves garlic, minced

  1 bag (12 ounces) peeled and deveined frozen medium shrimp, thawed and drained

  3 cups cooked brown or white rice

  1 can (14 to 19 ounces) black beans, rinsed and drained

  1 cup medium-spicy salsa

  ½ cup shredded reduced-fat Cheddar cheese

  Lime wedges, for serving

In a large, deep, nonstick skillet over medium heat, warm the oil. Add the garlic and cook, stirring, about 1 minute, or until fragrant. Add the shrimp and cook, stirring, 3 to 5 minutes, or until just pink.

Stir in the rice, beans, and salsa. Reduce the heat to low, cover, and cook about 5 minutes, or until the shrimp are pink and opaque in the thickest part and the mixture is hot and bubbly. Remove from the heat and sprinkle with the cheese. Serve with lime wedges.

Makes 4 servings

Per serving: *370 calories, 28 g protein, 40 g carbohydrate, 11 g fat, 140 mg cholesterol, 890 mg sodium, 7 g fiber*

Diet Exchanges: *0 milk, 1 vegetable, 0 fruit, 2 bread, 3 meat, 1½ fat*

3 Carb Choices

200 Calories

Pan-Seared Scallops with Red-Pepper Sauce

—Kim Tweed, Cape May Court House, New Jersey

Prep time: 10 minutes
Cook time: 9 minutes

2 tablespoons olive oil

1 medium onion, chopped

2 cloves garlic, minced

1 jar (7 ounces) roasted red peppers, drained

½ cup reduced-sodium, fat-free chicken broth

Salt

Ground black pepper

1½ pounds sea scallops, tough muscles at side removed, rinsed, and patted dry

1 can (11 ounces) mandarin oranges, drained

In a large nonstick skillet over medium heat, warm 1 tablespoon oil. Add the onion and garlic and cook, stirring, about 5 minutes, or until the onion has softened. Transfer the onion and garlic to the bowl of a food processor. Add the roasted peppers and broth. Process until smooth. Season to taste with salt and pepper.

Wipe the skillet clean and warm the remaining 1 tablespoon oil over medium-high heat until hot but not smoking. Add the scallops and cook, without turning, 2 minutes. Turn the scallops and add the mandarin oranges. Continue cooking 2 to 3 minutes longer, or until the scallops are opaque in the thickest part and the oranges are warm.

Serve immediately, drizzled with the red-pepper sauce.

Makes 4 servings

Per serving: *200 calories, 12 g protein, 18 g carbohydrate, 7 g fat, 20 mg cholesterol, 590 mg sodium, 1 g fiber*

Diet Exchanges: *0 milk, 2½ vegetable, ½ fruit, 0 bread, 1½ meat, 1½ fat*

1 Carb Choice

Suzanne's Lemon-Herb Steamed Fish

160 Calories

—Suzanne Vandyck, Santa Clara, California

"Foil steaming is one of my favorite methods of preparing fish, not only because of the glorious taste and texture, but because it is neat and clean. Since the fish is cooked in its own juices, there is no fat involved! I serve this often with a wild rice or bulgur salad or pilaf. You can use other herbs, such as thyme or dill, instead of the tarragon."

Prep time: 10 minutes
Bake time: 15 minutes

 6 haddock fillets (6 ounces each)
     Salt
     Ground black pepper
12 fresh tarragon sprigs or 1 teaspoon dried tarragon
 6 thin slices sweet white or red onion
 1 to 2 lemons, thinly sliced
 1 tablespoon capers, rinsed and drained
 2 tablespoons dry white wine
     Chopped fresh tarragon, for garnish (optional)

Preheat the oven to 400°F. Tear off six 12" pieces of foil. Fold each piece of foil cross-wise, then open up. Coat half of each piece with olive oil spray.

In the center of each sprayed half, place a haddock fillet. Season to taste with salt and pepper. On each, place 2 tarragon sprigs or some dried tarragon, 1 onion slice, 2 lemon slices, some capers, and a splash of wine.

Fold the unsprayed half of the foil over the fish and seal tightly. Place the packets on 2 baking sheets. Bake for 15 minutes, or until the packets are puffed and the haddock is just opaque in the thickest part (carefully open a packet to check). Garnish with chopped tarragon, if you like.

Makes 6 servings

Per serving: *160 calories, 32 g protein, 2 g carbohydrate, 1.5 g fat, 95 mg cholesterol, 160 mg sodium, 0 g fiber*

Diet Exchanges: *0 milk, 0 vegetable, 0 fruit, 0 bread, 5 meat, 0 fat*

0 Carb Choices

It Worked for Me!

Carrie Nelson

VITAL STATS

Weight lost: 45 pounds

Time to goal: 6 months

Greatest challenge: Finding time for workouts

Carrie Nelson started gaining weight after marriage, sometimes diving into a half-gallon of ice cream before bed and snacking on cake, potato chips, and doughnuts. Once she reached 200 pounds, Carrie hired a personal trainer at a gym, who helped her take off a good 25 pounds through weight lifting and aerobic exercise. The success was short-lived; the 3-month session expired, and without the weekly encouragement of her trainer, Carrie gained it all back.

In the back of her mind, she knew that being so heavy was endangering her health. Carrie busied herself with planning her 20-year high school reunion, and as she sent out the invitations in January 2003, she realized she had only 6 months to lose the weight. Humiliated at the prospect of greeting old classmates in her condition (at least 80 pounds heavier—and eight sizes larger—than they remembered her), she knew she had to at least try to drop the weight.

She joined a weight-loss club at work and volunteered to be in charge of the weekly weight charts. "We kept a scale in one classroom, and every Thursday morning before school started, we'd toss a dollar in the pot and do our weigh-ins. At the end of each month, the biggest loser won that month's earnings."

Carrie began counting calories and quickly realized that the large fries, medium soda, and Quarter Pounder with Cheese (1,290 calories) she was used to eating wouldn't fit into the 1,500-calories-per-day picture. "Giving up fast food was tough, but it wasn't nearly as difficult as I'd imagined once I started stocking the fridge with healthy alternatives such as grapes, apples, yogurt, lean turkey, and whole wheat bread."

Like most working moms, Carrie doesn't have oodles of spare time to devote to classes at the gym. So she did step aerobics with hand weights or walked on the treadmill in her living room while watching the evening news.

By her reunion 6 months later, she'd lost 32 pounds. "I felt surprisingly confident and charming, mingling with people I hadn't seen in decades. Plus, the high school friends I *had* seen all wanted to know what secret weight-loss plan I was on."

230 Calories

Crab-Stuffed Tilapia
with Tarragon "Cream" Sauce

—Elizabeth Martlock, Jim Thorpe, Pennsylvania

Prep time: 20 minutes
Cook time: 5 minutes
Bake time: 15 minutes

T I L A P I A

3 slices whole wheat bread, toasted
½ cup jarred roasted red peppers, chopped and well drained
½ cup shredded reduced-fat Cheddar cheese
¼ cup reduced-fat mayonnaise
2 tablespoons grated Parmesan cheese
2 teaspoons chopped fresh tarragon
Garlic powder
Salt
Ground black pepper
4 ounces lump crabmeat, picked over
6 large tilapia fillets (4 ounces each), each halved lengthwise
2 tablespoons dry white wine

S A U C E

1 cup fat-free half-and-half
1 tablespoon cornstarch
1 tablespoon dry sherry
Salt
Ground balck pepper
1 tablespoon chopped fresh tarragon

To make the tilapia: Preheat the oven to 350°F. Coat a roasting pan with olive oil spray.

Grind the toast to fine crumbs in a food processor. Transfer to a medium bowl and stir in the roasted peppers, Cheddar, mayonnaise, Parmesan, and tarragon. Season to taste with garlic powder, salt, and black pepper. Gently fold in the crabmeat.

Evenly divide the stuffing into 12 portions and place one in the center of each tilapia fillet. Roll the fillet, enclosing the stuffing, from the tapered end all the way to the opposite end. Arrange the rolls with the stuffing side up in the prepared pan. Drizzle with the wine and cover with foil. Bake about 15 minutes, or until the fish flakes easily and the stuffing is thoroughly heated.

Meanwhile, make the sauce: In a heavy medium saucepan, whisk together the half-and-half, cornstarch, sherry, Old Bay seasoning, garlic powder, and onion powder. Bring to a boil over medium-low heat, stirring constantly until slightly thickened, about 5 minutes. Remove from the heat and stir in the tarragon.

Spoon the sauce over the tilapia rolls just before serving.

Makes 6 servings

Per serving: *230 calories, 239 g protein, 14 g carbohydrate, 8 g fat, 50 mg cholesterol, 490 mg sodium, 0 g fiber*

Diet Exchanges: *0 milk, ½ vegetable, 0 fruit, 1 bread, ½ meat, 1 fat*

1 Carb Choice

Presto Pesto Chicken

260 Calories

—Rene Collins, Clute, Texas

"Pesto has a wonderful, rich flavor that goes well with chicken. It's heavy on fat and calories, but in this sauce a little adds a lot of flavor. Get a good brand made with heart-healthy olive oil."

Prep time: 10 minutes
Cook time: 13 minutes

1¼ **pounds thin chicken breast slices**
½ **teaspoon dried thyme**
½ **teaspoon salt**
¼ **teaspoon ground black pepper**
3 **tablespoons dry white wine or chicken broth**
1 **large clove garlic, minced**
½ **cup fat-free half-and-half**
3 **tablespoons pesto**
2 **plum tomatoes, chopped**
3 **tablespoons freshly grated Parmesan cheese**

Sprinkle the chicken on both sides with the thyme, salt, and pepper. Coat a large non-stick skillet with olive oil spray and warm over medium-high heat. Add the chicken, in batches if necessary, and cook, turning once, about 5 minutes, or until browned. Transfer to a plate and cover to keep warm.

Add the wine or broth and garlic to the pan drippings. Cook over medium-low heat, stirring, about 2 minutes, or until the liquid is reduced. Add the half-and-half and bring to a simmer, stirring. Cook about 5 minutes, or until reduced slightly.

Stir in the pesto. Add the chicken and any juices, and warm through. Sprinkle with the chopped tomatoes and Parmesan.

Makes 4 servings

Per serving: *260 calories, 37 g protein, 6 g carbohydrate, 9 g fat, 90 mg cholesterol, 580 mg sodium, 0 g fiber*

Diet Exchanges: *0 milk, ½ vegetable, 0 fruit, 0 bread, 5 meat, 1 fat*

½ Carb Choice

370 Calories

Stir-Fry in a Tortilla

—Patsie Clark, Abingdon, Virginia

"My husband and I both enjoy this meal and are still able to lose weight."

Prep time: 15 minutes
Cook time: 10 minutes

 1 tablespoon olive oil
 1 red bell pepper, thinly sliced
 1 yellow or orange bell pepper, thinly sliced
 1 box (8 ounces) sliced white button mushrooms
 ½ cup sliced red onion
 ¾ pound boneless, skinless chicken breast halves, cooked and cut into bite-size pieces
 2 tablespoons chopped fresh parsley
 1 teaspoon chili powder
 ½ teaspoon ground cumin
   Salt
   Ground black pepper
 8 whole wheat tortillas (8" in diameter)
 ¼ cup whipped fat-free cream cheese
 ½ cup shredded reduced-fat Cheddar cheese

In a large nonstick skillet over medium-high heat, warm the oil. Add the bell peppers, mushrooms, and red onion, and cook, stirring frequently, about 5 minutes, or until tender. Reduce the heat to medium and cover. Cook 5 minutes longer. Add the chicken, parsley, chili powder, and cumin, and season to taste with salt and pepper. Toss to mix well. Cook, stirring, until the chicken is heated through.

Meanwhile, warm the tortillas in the microwave or oven according to package directions. Spread each tortilla with cream cheese, then spoon one-eighth of the chicken mixture on the bottom halves of each. Top evenly with the Cheddar. Roll up the tortillas, and secure with toothpicks, if necessary.

Makes 4 servings (2 tortillas per serving)

Per serving: *370 calories, 34 g protein, 49 g carbohydrate, 9 g fat, 90 mg cholesterol, 500 mg sodium, 5 g fiber*

Diet Exchanges: *0 milk, 1½ vegetable, 0 fruit, 2 bread, 3½ meat, 1 fat*

3 Carb Choices

220 Calories

Quick Ginger Rice and Veggies with Chicken

—Tonya Froemel, Hayward, Wisconsin

"This is a quick meal that I can make on hectic nights when I have little time to cook. I cook this instead of getting takeout."

Prep time: 5 minutes
Cook time: 18 minutes
Microwave time: 10 minutes

½ cup instant brown rice

2 cups + 2 tablespoons water

¼ teaspoon salt

1¼ pounds boneless, skinless chicken breast halves, cut into 1" pieces

3 tablespoons reduced-sodium soy sauce
Ground black pepper

1 bag (16 ounces) frozen stir-fry vegetables

½ teaspoon ground ginger

In a medium saucepan over high heat, stir together the rice, 2 cups water, and the salt. Bring to a boil. Reduce the heat to low, cover, and simmer for 10 minutes, or until the liquid has been absorbed. Let stand for 5 minutes, covered.

Meanwhile, in a large microwaveable bowl, toss the chicken with 1 tablespoon soy sauce, and season to taste with pepper. Cover with a lid or vented plastic wrap and microwave on high, stirring twice, for 3 to 5 minutes, or until no longer pink.

Add the frozen vegetables, ginger, remaining 2 tablespoons water, and remaining 2 tablespoons soy sauce. Cover and microwave on high, stirring 2 or 3 times, until the vegetables are heated through, about 5 minutes longer.

Fluff the rice with a fork. Serve the chicken and vegetables over the rice.

Makes 4 servings

Per serving: *220 calories, 37 g protein, 14 g carbohydrate, 2½ g fat, 80 mg cholesterol, 660 mg sodium, 3 g fiber*

Diet Exchanges: *0 milk, 1½ vegetable, 0 fruit, 0 bread, 5 meat, 0 fat*

1 Carb Choice

Chicken Cacciatore Pasta

—Lori DeJulia, Sharpsville, Pennsylvania

Prep time: 10 minutes
Cook time: 28 minutes

  2 tablespoons olive oil

1½ pounds boneless, skinless chicken breast halves, cut into bite-size chunks

  1 large green bell pepper, thinly sliced

  3 cloves garlic, minced

¾ teaspoon dried oregano

½ teaspoon crushed red-pepper flakes

  Salt

  Ground black pepper

  1 box (10 ounces) baby portobello mushrooms, quartered

  2 tablespoons dry white wine or chicken broth

  1 can (28 ounces) crushed tomatoes

½ pound whole wheat pasta

In a large, deep nonstick skillet over medium-high heat, warm the oil. Add the chicken and bell pepper, and sprinkle with the garlic, oregano, and crushed red pepper. Season to taste with salt and black pepper. Cook, stirring often, for 5 minutes, or until the chicken is lightly browned.

Add the mushrooms and wine or broth. Cook, stirring often, for 8 minutes, or until the mushrooms are tender. Stir in the tomatoes and bring to a boil. Reduce the heat to low and simmer, uncovered, for 15 minutes, or until the sauce is lightly thickened.

Meanwhile, cook the pasta according to the package directions. Drain and transfer to the skillet. Toss to mix well.

Makes 6 servings

Per serving: *360 calories, 36 g protein, 37 g carbohydrate, 7 g fat, 65 mg cholesterol, 260 mg sodium, 8 g fiber*

Diet Exchanges: *0 milk, 2½ vegetable, 0 fruit, 0 bread, 4 meat, 1 fat*

2½ Carb Choices

340 Calories

Grilled Chicken with Red Onion Confit

—Elizabeth Martlock, Jim Thorpe, Pennsylvania

Get a taste of the outdoors by preparing this tasty chicken dish on the grill!

Prep time: 10 minutes
Marinating time: 30 minutes
Cook time: 28 minutes

6 **boneless, skinless chicken breast halves (5 ounces each)**

4 **tablespoons olive oil**

1 **packet (¾ ounce) taco seasoning**

1 **teaspoon coarse-ground black pepper**

3 **medium red onions, halved and thinly sliced**

2 **tablespoons brown sugar**
  Salt

In a large zip-top freezer bag, combine the chicken, 2 tablespoons oil, the taco seasoning, and pepper. Seal the bag, and squeeze the bag to mix the seasoning and oil and to coat the chicken. Place the bag on a baking sheet and marinate in the refrigerator for 30 minutes or longer.

In a large, deep nonstick skillet over medium heat, warm the remaining 2 tablespoons oil. Add the red onions. Sprinkle with the brown sugar and salt to taste, and toss to mix well. Reduce the heat to medium-low and cook, stirring occasionally, 20 to 25 minutes, or until the onions are tender and caramelized. Remove from the heat and cover to keep warm.

Heat a barbecue grill to medium-hot. Grill the chicken (discard bag with leftover marinade), making grill marks on the side, and turning once, for about 8 minutes, or until a thermometer inserted in the thickest part registers 170°F and the juices run clear. Serve with the red onion confit.

Makes 6 servings

Per serving: *340 calories, 33 g protein, 12 g carbohydrate, 11 g fat, 80 mg cholesterol, 390 mg sodium, 0 g fiber*

Diet Exchanges: *0 milk, 1 vegetable, 0 fruit, ½ bread, 5 meat, 2 fat*

1 Carb Choice

200 Calories

Grilled Buffalo "Wings"

—Brenda Cole, Reisterstown, Maryland

"My family LOVES buffalo wings. But deep-fried foods and weight loss do not go hand-in-hand. Unwilling to give up our treasured wings, I came up with this recipe for near-guiltless noshing! After a year of making them this way, my family doesn't even like restaurant wings anymore."

Prep time: 10 minutes
Cook time: 4 minutes

1 **pound chicken tenders**
Salt
Ground black pepper
⅓ **cup prepared Buffalo wing sauce**
4 **ribs celery, cut into sticks**
4 **carrots, cut into sticks**
2 **kirby cucumbers, cut into spears**
⅓ **cup fat-free ranch dressing**

Season the chicken tenders to taste with salt and pepper.

Coat a ridged grill pan with olive oil spray and heat over medium-high heat, or heat an electric countertop griller. Grill the chicken, turning once, about 4 minutes, or until browned and no longer pink in the thickest part. Cut into bite-sized pieces. Transfer to a bowl and toss with the Buffalo sauce.

Place the chicken on a platter with the celery, carrots, cucumbers, and the ranch dressing for dipping. Serve with a good supply of wooden picks.

Makes 4 servings

Per serving: *200 calories, 29 g protein, 21 g carbohydrate, 1 g fat, 65 mg cholesterol, 1,020 mg sodium, 5 g fiber*

Diet Exchanges: *0 milk, 2½ vegetable, 0 fruit, ½ bread, 3 meat, 0 fat*

1½ Carb Choices

200 Calories

Grilled Cilantro-Lime Chicken

—Christie Neal, Auburn, Washington

This preparation adds some variety to bone-in chicken breasts without weighing them down with calories and fat.

Prep time: 10 minutes
Marinate time: 4 hours
Cook time: 10 minutes

½ cup fresh lime juice

¼ cup chopped fresh cilantro

2 tablespoons olive oil

4 bone-in chicken breast halves (8 ounces each), skinned

Salt

Ground black pepper

Lime wedges, for serving

In a shallow baking dish, mix the lime juice, cilantro, and oil. Season the chicken to taste with salt and pepper. Add the chicken to the lime mixture and turn to coat. Cover and marinate in the refrigerator, turning once or twice, for about 4 hours.

Heat a barbecue grill to medium-hot, or preheat the broiler and coat a broiler-pan rack with cooking spray. Grill or broil the chicken, turning once, 10 to 12 minutes, or until a thermometer inserted in the thickest part registers 170°F and the juices run clear. Serve with the lime wedges.

Makes 4 servings

Per serving: *200 calories, 27 g protein, 3 g carbohydrate, 8 g fat, 70 mg cholesterol, 80 mg sodium, 0 g fiber*

Diet Exchanges: *0 milk, 0 vegetable, 0 fruit, 0 bread, 4 meat, 1½ fat*

0 Carb Choices

420 Calories

Baked Chicken with Brown Rice and Veggies

—Tara Duncan, Calgary, Alberta, Canada

"Because this is so easy to make, it stops me from picking up fast food on the way home from work."

Prep time: 10 minutes
Bake time: 1 hour and 20 minutes

1 cup long- or short-grain brown rice
2 cups reduced-sodium, fat-free chicken broth
1 can (10¾ ounces) reduced-fat, reduced-sodium cream of mushroom soup
1 teaspoon dried thyme
   Salt
   Ground black pepper
4 bone-in chicken leg quarters (8 ounces each), skinned
½ teaspoon ground paprika
2 cups frozen mixed peas and carrots
½ cup sliced scallions

Preheat the oven to 350°F.

In a 13" × 9" glass baking dish, stir together the rice, broth, soup and thyme, and season to taste with salt and pepper. Place the chicken pieces on top, and sprinkle with the paprika and additional salt and pepper.

Cover the dish with foil. Bake 1 hour. Uncover and bake 15 minutes longer, or until the rice is tender, and a thermometer inserted in the thickest part of the chicken registers 170°F and the juices run clear. Transfer the chicken to a serving dish and cover to keep warm. Stir the peas and carrots and scallions into the rice. Cover and bake 5 minutes longer, or until heated through. Place the chicken on top of the rice to serve.

Makes 4 servings

Per serving: *420 calories, 35 g protein, 51 g carbohydrate, 8 g fat, 105 mg cholesterol, 740 mg sodium, 5 g fiber*

Diet Exchanges: *0 milk, 2 vegetable, 0 fruit, 3 bread, 3½ meat, 1 fat*

3½ Carb Choices

Basil and Lemon–Roasted Chicken Breasts

250 Calories

—Cheryl Doubinin, Cumberland, British Columbia, Canada

Make this a true oven dinner...start baking white or sweet potatoes while you're prepping the chicken. Medium-size potatoes will be done in about an hour.

Prep time: 15 minutes
Bake time: 30 minutes

    1 teaspoon lemon peel
    2 tablespoons lemon juice
    1 cup packed fresh basil leaves
    2 cloves garlic, sliced
    1 tablespoon olive oil
    1 tablespoon water or fat-free chicken broth, if needed
    4 bone-in chicken breast halves (8 ounces each), skinned
      Salt
      Ground black pepper
    1 pint small cherry or grape tomatoes, stemmed
      Lemon wedges, for serving

Preheat the oven to 400°F. Coat a shallow baking pan with olive oil spray.

In a food processor, combine the lemon peel and juice, basil, garlic, and oil. Process until finely pureed. Stir in the water or broth to loosen the mixture, if needed.

Place the chicken breasts in the prepared pan. Season to taste with salt and pepper. Spoon the basil mixture evenly over the chicken. Scatter the cherry or grape tomatoes in the pan around the chicken.

Bake, uncovered, spooning the pan juices over the chicken once or twice, for 30 to 35 minutes, or until a thermometer inserted in the thickest part of the chicken registers 170°F and the juices run clear. Serve with the tomatoes, any pan juices, and lemon wedges.

Makes 4 servings

Per serving: *250 calories, 43 g protein, 5 g carbohydrate, 6 g fat, 105 mg cholesterol, 130 mg sodium, 1 g fiber*

Diet Exchanges: *0 milk, ½ vegetable, 0 fruit, 0 bread, 6 meat, ½ fat*

0 Carb Choices

170 Calories

Lemon-Pepper Chicken

—Marilyn Wons, Destin, Florida

"This is so delicious and has so few calories. It is very simple to make which gives me more time to exercise!"

Prep time: 5 minutes
Bake time: 35 minutes

- 1 **bag (6 ounces) baby spinach**
- 4 **boneless, skinless chicken breast halves (5 ounces each)**
- 2 **teaspoons lemon-pepper seasoning**
  Salt
  Lemon wedges, for serving

Preheat the oven to 350°F. Coat a shallow 13" × 9" baking dish with cooking spray. Spread the spinach on the bottom of the prepared baking dish. Place the chicken breasts on top. Sprinkle generously with lemon-pepper seasoning and season to taste with salt.

Cover the pan with foil and bake for 35 to 40 minutes, or until the spinach has cooked down and wilted, a thermometer inserted in the thickest part of the chicken registers 170°F, and the juices run clear. Serve with lemon wedges.

Makes 4 servings

Per serving: *170 calories, 34 g protein, 5 g carbohydrate, 2 g fat, 80 mg cholesterol, 390 mg sodium, 2 g fiber*

Diet Exchanges: *0 milk, 1 vegetable, 0 fruit, 0 bread, 5 meat, 0 fat*

0 Carb Choices

Quick and Easy Curries

Maya Kaimal's superb, all-natural, fresh Indian simmer sauces are your key to a quick, fabulous meal. The vibrant flavors, ranging from mild to spicy, include Tikka Masala, Coconut Curry, Tamarind Curry, and Vindaloo. The nutrition profile is a touch high, but simmered with plenty of veggies (frozen are great) and lean protein (browned if you want in nonstick cooking spray) and spooned atop brown basmati rice, the dish will serve six instead of four. For a spicy-rich baking sauce, pour one over chicken, fish, or shrimp. Cover and bake at 425°F. Maya Kaimal's Indian Simmer Sauces are found at Whole Foods, gourmet and Indian shops, and from igourmet.com. For a store locator, go to mayakaimal.com.

Here are some great ways with Indian Simmer Sauces.

Chicken Tikka Masala: Lightly brown 2 pounds chicken or turkey breast cubes in cooking spray in a heavy skillet. Add a sliced zucchini and sliced red bell pepper; toss until wilted. Add Tikka Masala Sauce and 1 cup frozen peas; cover and cook 5 minutes. Sprinkle with sliced scallions; serve over brown basmati rice.

Baked Chicken Vindaloo: Pour Vindaloo sauce over 2½ pounds skinned, bone-in chicken thighs or drumsticks in a roasting pan. Cover and bake at 425°F about 40 minutes. Serve over rice with plain nonfat yogurt to cut the heat.

Vegetable Curry: Boil 1 large peeled, cubed sweet potato in ½ water, covered, until nearly tender. Add 2 large sliced carrots, 2 cups broccoli florets, and 1 cup frozen string beans; cover and cook 6 to 8 minutes, until tender. Add Tamarind Curry Sauce; cover and simmer 5 minutes.

Shrimp-Spinach Coconut Curry: Simmer 2 pounds peeled shrimp in Coconut Curry Sauce, covered, 3 to 4 minutes, until cooked through. Stir in a bag of spinach and cook until wilted. Serve over rice with chopped peanuts, tomato and cucumber, and sliced scallions.

230 Calories

Garlic-and-Herb-Crusted Chicken

—Elena Dodge, Erie, Pennsylvania

"This recipe kept me going because it's so easy to make—and tasty!"

Prep time: 5 minutes
Bake time: 30 minutes

  4 teaspoons olive oil
  ½ cup Italian-style dry bread crumbs
  ½ teaspoon chicken seasoning
  ¼ teaspoon ground black pepper
  4 boneless, skinless chicken breast halves
    (5 ounces each)
    Butter-flavored garlic-and-herb spray

Preheat the oven to 350°F. Coat a rimmed baking sheet with 2 teaspoons oil.

Mix the bread crumbs, chicken seasoning, and pepper in a zip-top plastic bag. Coat both sides of the chicken with garlic-and-herb spray. One piece at a time, add the chicken to the bag and shake until well coated. Place the chicken on the prepared baking sheet.

Drizzle the chicken with the remaining 2 teaspoons oil. Bake for 30 to 40 minutes, or until the crumbs are browned, a thermometer inserted in the thickest part of the chicken registers 170°F, and the juices run clear.

Makes 4 servings

Per serving: *230 calories, 35 g protein, 10 g carbohydrate, 5 g fat, 80 mg cholesterol, 360 mg sodium, 0 g fiber*

Diet Exchanges: *0 milk, 0 vegetable, 0 fruit, 1 bread, 5 meat, ½ fat*

1 Carb Choice

····· SECRETS OF WEIGHT-LOSS WINNERS ·········

• Use a luncheon plate instead of a dinner plate—what fits on the smaller plate is all you get!
    —Unita Esau, Meadow Lake, Saskatchewan, Canada

• When it comes to exercise, don't overdo it at first! An injury early on will only lead to less exercise later. Start slowly and gradually increase your level of exercise as you get into shape.
    —Michael Oelrich, Chicago, Illinois

250 Calories

Tuscan Country Chicken
—Saundra McKenzie, Phoenix, Arizona

"I have lost 45 pounds so far, and I make this every Sunday night and eat the leftovers off and on during the week. It has a great taste and I think it has really contributed to my weight loss."

Prep time: 10 minutes
Roast time: 1 hour 15 minutes

  1 **chicken (3½ to 4 pounds), rinsed, giblets reserved for another use**
    Salt
    Ground black pepper
 12 **fresh bay leaves or 6 dried**
  1 **lemon, quartered, plus extra wedges for serving**
  2 **cloves garlic, halved**

Preheat the oven to 400°F. Arrange a rack in a roasting pan.

Pat the chicken dry with paper towels. Season it inside and out with salt and pepper to taste. With your fingers, loosen the skin over the chicken breast and slip 11 fresh or 5 dried bay leaves under the skin. In the cavity, place the lemon quarters, garlic, and remaining bay leaf. Secure the cavity with toothpicks or a wooden skewer.

Place the chicken on the rack in the pan. Roast for 1 hour and 15 minutes to 1 hour and 30 minutes, or until the chicken is well browned, a thermometer inserted in the thigh, not touching bone, registers 180°F, and the juices run clear.

Transfer the chicken to a serving platter and let stand for 10 minutes. Discard the bay leaves. Carve the chicken, remove the skin, and serve with lemon wedges.

Makes 4 servings

Per serving: *250 calories, 46 g protein, 0 g carbohydrate, 6 g fat, 145 mg cholesterol, 170 mg sodium, 0 g fiber*

Diet Exchanges: *0 milk, 0 vegetable, 0 fruit, 0 bread, 6 meat, 1½ fat*

0 Carb Choices

240 Calories

Honey-Apple Chicken

—Jan Miller, Hillsborough, New Jersey

"This recipe also satisfied my family's sweet tooth, leaving no need for dessert."

Prep time: 10 minutes
Bake time: 45 minutes

1 chicken (3½ pounds), quartered and skinned (reserve wings and giblets for another use)
1 teaspoon ground cinnamon
½ teaspoon ground nutmeg
¼ teaspoon ground black pepper
2 tart apples, cored and chopped
½ cup dried apple rings, roughly chopped
¼ cup apple juice
2 tablespoons reduced-sodium soy sauce
2 tablespoons honey

Preheat the oven to 350°F.

Place the chicken pieces in a 13" × 9" baking dish or casserole, and season with the cinnamon, nutmeg, and pepper. Sprinkle the fresh and dried apple pieces on top. In a cup, stir together the apple juice, soy sauce, and honey, and pour evenly over the chicken.

Cover with foil and bake for 30 minutes. Uncover, spoon the sauce over the chicken, and bake 15 minutes longer, or until a thermometer inserted in the thickest part registers 170°F and the juices run clear. Serve the chicken with the apples and pan juices.

Makes 4 servings

Per serving: *240 calories, 28 g protein, 28 g carbohydrate, 2 g fat, 70 mg cholesterol, 360 mg sodium, 3 g fiber*

Diet Exchanges: *0 milk, 0 vegetable, 1 fruit, ½ bread, 4 meat, 0 fat*

2 Carb Choices

340 Calories

Stuffed Peppers

—Leona Carloni, Trumbull, Connecticut

Prep time: 20 minutes
Cook time: 18 minutes
Bake time: 40 minutes

½ pound lean crumbled turkey sausage
1 tablespoon olive oil
1 large onion, chopped
1 rib celery, thinly sliced
1 cup chopped white button mushrooms
3 cups cornbread stuffing mix or cubes
1½ cup water or reduced-sodium, fat-free chicken broth
2 large egg whites
Salt
Ground black pepper
8 Italian frying peppers (about 2 pounds)

In a large nonstick skillet over medium-high heat, cook the turkey sausage, breaking it up with the back of a spoon, 8 to 10 minutes, or until no longer pink. With a slotted spoon, transfer the sausage to a bowl.

In the same skillet over medium heat, warm the oil. Add the onion, celery, and mushrooms. Cook, stirring often, about 8 minutes, or until tender. Remove from the heat. Stir in the stuffing mix, water or broth, egg whites, and sausage and any of its juices. Season to taste with salt and pepper. Set aside to cool for a few minutes.

Meanwhile, preheat the oven to 375°F. Cut the tops off the peppers and reserve. Remove the seeds and ribs from the peppers. (Peppers may be blanched for 3 to 5 minutes for extra tenderness.)

Spoon one-eighth (about ½ cup) of the stuffing into each pepper and replace the tops, securing with toothpicks. Arrange the peppers in a 13" × 9" baking dish. Pour ½ cup water in the pan around the peppers. Cover the pan with foil. Bake for about 40 minutes, or until the peppers are tender and the stuffing is piping hot.

Makes 4 servings

Per serving: *340 calories, 21 g protein, 46 g carbohydrate, 9 g fat, 35 mg cholesterol, 940 mg sodium, 11 g fiber*

Diet Exchanges: *0 milk, 3½ vegetable, 0 fruit, 2 bread, ½ meat, 1 fat*

3 Carb Choices

Very Veggie Skillet Casserole

—Rene Collins, Clute, Texas

"You don't have to light the oven to have a healthy, nutritious, and good-for-your-waist stove-top casserole."

Prep time: 15 minutes
Cook time: 33 minutes

¾ **pound lean ground turkey breast**
2 **tablespoons olive oil**
½ **cup chopped onion**
2 **cloves garlic, minced**
½ **cup finely chopped yellow summer squash**
½ **cup finely chopped tomato**
½ **cup sliced celery**
½ **cup sliced carrot**
  Salt
  Ground black pepper
1 **cup instant brown rice**
1½ **cups water**
1 **teaspoon reduced-sodium chicken bouillon granules**
4 **cups baby spinach**

In a large, deep nonstick skillet over medium-high heat, cook the ground turkey, breaking it up with the back of a spoon, for 8 to 10 minutes, or until no longer pink. With a slotted spoon, transfer the turkey to a medium bowl.

In the same skillet over medium heat, warm the oil. Add the onion and garlic. Cook, stirring often, 5 minutes, or until the onion is softened. Add the squash, tomato, celery, and carrot. Cook, stirring often, about 5 minutes, or until the vegetables are crisp-tender.

Return the turkey and any juices to the pan. Season to taste with salt and pepper, and stir to combine. Stir in the rice, water, and bouillon granules. Bring to a boil. Reduce the heat to low, cover, and cook about 15 minutes, or until the rice is tender. Stir in the spinach, cover, and cook about 1 minute longer, or until the spinach is wilted.

Makes 4 servings

Per serving: *250 calories, 24 g protein, 20 g carbohydrate, 9 g fat, 35 mg cholesterol, 120 mg sodium, 3 g fiber*

Diet Exchanges: *0 milk, 1½ vegetable, 0 fruit, 0 bread, 2½ meat, 1½ fat*

1 Carb Choice

410 Calories

Healthy and Hearty Pasta

—Rupali Lubchansky, North Brunswick, New Jersey

"Before I started dieting, my husband and I would eat heaping plates of regular pasta, with tons of sauce and cheese. Once I became seriously committed to my weight-loss journey (22 pounds so far), we reinvented our entire style of cooking. We began purchasing whole wheat products, low-fat cheeses, tons of vegetables, and even an affordable food scale. When we used the food scale, we were shocked to see what "real" portions were supposed to be!"

Prep time: 15 minutes
Cook time: 23 minutes

½ **pound whole wheat rotini or penne pasta**

½ **pound lean ground turkey breast**

1 **tablespoon olive oil**

1 **Cubanelle pepper or any pepper you prefer, chopped**

4 **scallions, chopped**

2 **cloves garlic, minced**

1 **can (14½ ounces) diced tomatoes**

2 **tablespoons dry red wine (optional)**

1 **teaspoon dried basil**

½ **teaspoon dried oregano**

Salt

Ground black pepper

4 **ounces firm marinated or smoked tofu, drained and finely chopped**

½ **cup shredded part-skim mozzarella**

Cook the pasta according to the package directions. Scoop out ½ cup pasta-cooking water and reserve. Drain the pasta and return to the cooking pot to keep warm.

Coat a large, deep nonstick skillet with olive oil spray and warm over medium-high heat. Add the ground turkey and cook, breaking it up with the back of a spoon, 8 to 10 minutes, or until no longer pink. Transfer to a bowl.

In the same skillet over medium heat, warm the oil. Add the Cubanelle pepper, scallions, and garlic. Cook, stirring often, about 5 minutes, or until tender. Stir in the tomatoes (and their juices), wine (if using), basil, and oregano; season to taste with salt and pepper. Bring to a boil. Reduce the heat and simmer 10 minutes, or until lightly thickened. Stir in the turkey, and any juices, and the tofu; warm through.

Add the pasta and reserved pasta water. Toss to mix well. Sprinkle with the mozzarella.

Makes 4 servings

Per serving: *410 calories, 34 g protein, 51 g carbohydrate, 10 g fat, 30 mg cholesterol, 360 mg sodium, 8 g fiber*

Diet Exchanges: *0 milk, 1 vegetable, 0 fruit, 0 bread, 3 meat, 1½ fat*

3½ Carb Choices

420 Calories

Skinny Spaghetti

—Arthena Anderson, St. John's, Newfoundland, Canada

Prep time: 10 minutes
Cook time: 26 minutes

½ pound whole wheat spaghetti
½ pound lean ground turkey breast
1 tablespoon olive oil
1 green bell pepper, chopped
1 red bell pepper, chopped
1 medium onion, chopped
1 can (28 ounces) crushed tomatoes in puree
Salt
Ground black pepper
½ cup part-skim ricotta cheese

Cook the spaghetti according to the package directions. Drain the pasta and return to the cooking pot to keep warm.

Coat a large nonstick skillet with olive oil spray and warm over medium-high heat. Add the ground turkey and cook, breaking it up with the back of a spoon, for 8 to 10 minutes, or until no longer pink. Transfer to a bowl.

In the same skillet over medium heat, warm the oil. Add the bell peppers and onion, and cook, stirring often, about 8 minutes, or until tender. Stir in the tomatoes and turkey with any juices. Season to taste with salt and pepper. Bring to a boil. Reduce the heat to low and simmer for 10 minutes, or until lightly thickened. Add the pasta to the skillet and toss to mix well. Spoon the ricotta cheese on top.

Makes 4 servings

Per serving: *420 calories, 30 g protein, 65 g carbohydrate, 8 g fat, 30 mg cholesterol, 340 mg sodium, 12 g fiber*

Diet Exchanges: *0 milk, 3½ vegetable, 0 fruit, 2½ bread, 2½ meat, 1 fat*

4 Carb Choices

Smoked Turkey Sausage Rigatoni

330 Calories

—Christi Long, Cleveland, Tennessee

"Can also be served with whole grain toast with light butter and garlic powder."

Prep time: 10 minutes
Cook time: 20 minutes

- ½ **pound rigatoni**
- ½ **pound smoked lean turkey sausage, cut into ½"-thick slices**
- 1 **medium onion, thinly sliced**
- 1 **can (14½ ounces) petite diced tomatoes**
- 1 **cup prepared marinara sauce**

Cook the pasta according to the package directions. Drain the pasta and return to the cooking pot to keep warm.

Coat a large, deep nonstick skillet with olive oil spray and warm over medium-high heat. Add the sausage and onion, and cook, stirring often, about 10 minutes, or until the sausage is browned and heated through. Drain off any fat.

Stir in the tomatoes (and their juices) and marinara sauce, and bring to a boil. Reduce the heat and simmer about 10 minutes, or until the sauce is lightly thickened. Add the pasta and toss to mix well.

Makes 4 servings

Per serving: *330 calories, 13 g protein, 60 g carbohydrate, 3 g fat, 10 mg cholesterol, 910 mg sodium, 4 g fiber*

Diet Exchanges: *0 milk, 1½ vegetable, 0 fruit, 3 bread, ½ meat, 0 fat*

4 Carb Choices

SECRETS OF WEIGHT-LOSS WINNERS

• Forget about the car. Walk briskly, both indoors and outdoors, whenever possible.

—Lori Sexton, Innisfil, Ontario, Canada

• Ban junk food from your house. You won't be tempted to eat what isn't there!

—Belinda Moore, Etta, Missouri

Dee-Ritos

430 Calories

—Dee Sanders, DeQueen, Arkansas

"I snack on apples, fruit smoothies, and other fruits throughout the day, and make this my main meal. I walk in the afternoons. Before you know it, the weight starts coming off."

Prep time: 15 minutes
Cook time: 12 minutes

¾ **pound 95% lean ground beef**

⅓ **cup water**

1 **package (1¼ ounces) taco seasoning mix**

4 **whole wheat soft taco wraps (8" in diameter)**

1 **can (16 ounces) fat-free refried beans, heated**

2 **cups baby spinach leaves**

1 **large tomato, chopped**

½ **cup shredded reduced-fat Cheddar cheese**

¼ **cup chopped sweet red or white onion**

In a large nonstick skillet over medium-high heat, cook the ground beef, breaking it up with the back of a spoon, for about 10 minutes, or until no longer pink. Drain in a colander and return to the skillet. Add the water and taco seasoning and cook and stir for 2 to 3 minutes, or until thickened.

One by one, heat the taco wraps in a warm skillet over medium heat about 10 seconds on each side, or until hot and pliable. (Or layer the wraps between paper towels and microwave on high 40 to 60 seconds, or until warmed.) Spread the wraps evenly with the refried beans, and spoon the beef mixture on top. Top evenly with the spinach, tomato, Cheddar, and onion. Roll up each wrap, folding in the sides.

Makes 4 servings

Per serving: *430 calories, 33 g protein, 49 g carbohydrate, 10 g fat, 65 mg cholesterol, 1,200 mg sodium, 11 g fiber*

Diet Exchanges: *0 milk, ½ vegetable, 0 fruit, 1½ bread, 3 meat, 1 fat*

3 Carb Choices

380 Calories

Tamale Pie

—Chris Detris, Breinigsville, Pennsylvania

This easy and comforting dish is a snap to prepare.

Prep time: 10 minutes
Cook time: 37 minutes

1+ tablespoon olive oil

 1 pound 95% lean ground beef

 1 can (15 ounces) no-salt-added black beans, rinsed and drained

 1 can (8 ounces) no-salt-added tomato sauce or salsa

½ cup water

 1 package (1¼ ounces) lower-sodium taco seasoning

 1 package (8 ounces) corn muffin mix

 1 large egg

⅓ cup fat-free milk

 1 cup shredded reduced-fat Cheddar cheese

 2 tablespoons sliced scallion

In a large nonstick skillet over medium-high heat, warm the oil. Add the ground beef and cook, breaking it up with the back of a spoon, about 10 minutes, or until no longer pink. Drain in a colander and return to the skillet. Stir in the black beans, tomato sauce or salsa, water, and taco seasoning; bring to a boil. Reduce the heat to medium-low, cover, and simmer for 5 minutes.

Meanwhile, in a small bowl, stir together the corn muffin mix, egg, and milk until blended. Drop the batter in small spoonfuls over the meat-and-bean mixture. Cover and simmer over medium-low heat about 15 minutes, or until the cornbread is firm and dry when lightly pressed. Sprinkle with the Cheddar and scallions. Cover and cook about 2 minutes longer, or until the cheese has melted. Let stand for about 15 minutes before serving.

Makes 6 servings

Per serving: *380 calories, 24 g protein, 39 g carbohydrate, 14 g fat, 100 mg cholesterol, 630 mg sodium, 3 g fiber*

Diet Exchanges: *0 milk, 0 vegetable, 0 fruit, 2 bread, 3 meat, 1½ fat*

2½ Carb Choices

360
Calories

Beef Stew on Toast

—Melinda Lauck, El Paso, Texas

"Sometimes I need some comfort food—and this hits the spot."

Prep time: 15 minutes
Cook time: 30 minutes

1 **pound 95% lean ground beef**
Salt
Ground black pepper
1½ **tablespoons canola oil**
1 **medium onion, chopped**
2 **cloves garlic, minced**
2 **cups shredded cabbage**
1 **can (14½ ounces) fat-free, reduced-sodium beef broth**
2 **tablespoons all-purpose flour**
1 **can (14½ ounces) diced tomatoes**
1 **bag (14 ounces) frozen green beans, thawed and drained**
4 **slices whole wheat bread, toasted and diagonally halved**

In a large, deep nonstick skillet over medium-high heat, cook the ground beef, breaking it up with the back of a wooden spoon, for about 10 minutes, or until no longer pink. Season to taste with salt and pepper. Drain the beef in a colander.

Add the oil to the same skillet and warm over medium heat. Add the onion and garlic, and cook, stirring often, 3 to 4 minutes, or until tender. Add the cabbage and cook, stirring often, about 5 minutes, or until tender and lightly browned.

In a small bowl, whisk the broth into the flour until blended and smooth. Gradually stir into the skillet. Bring to a boil, stirring often. Stir in the tomatoes (and their juices). Cook, stirring occasionally, about 5 minutes, or until lightly thickened. Add the green beans and ground beef to the skillet. Cook for about 7 minutes, or until heated through and bubbly.

Arrange 2 toast triangles on each of 4 plates. Spoon the beef stew evenly on top.

Makes 4 servings

Per serving: *360 calories, 32 g protein, 31 g carbohydrate, 12 g fat, 70 mg cholesterol, 660 mg sodium, 6 g fiber*

Diet Exchanges: *0 milk, 3 vegetable, 0 fruit, 1 bread, 4 meat, 2 fat*

2 Carb Choices

Karen's Rice

—Karen Preston, Smithville, Ontario, Canada

"This recipe keeps me full. It has enough fat in it that I'm not hungry. My kids really love it when they know this is for dinner."

Prep time: 10 minutes
Cook time: 25 minutes

1½ **pounds 95% lean ground beef**

1 **medium onion, chopped**

1 **green bell pepper, chopped**

2 **cans (10¾ ounces each) reduced-fat, reduced-sodium cream of tomato soup**

½ **soup can of water**

¼ **cup cider vinegar**

2 **tablespoons brown sugar**

2 **tablespoons Worcestershire sauce**

½ **teaspoon ground black pepper**

1 **cup white or brown rice**

½ **cup shredded part-skim mozzarella cheese**

In a large nonstick skillet over medium-high heat, cook the ground beef with the onion and bell pepper, breaking up the meat with the back of a spoon, for about 10 minutes, or until the meat is no longer pink and the vegetables are tender. Drain in a colander and return to the skillet.

In a medium bowl, whisk together the tomato soup, water, vinegar, brown sugar, Worcestershire, and black pepper. Add the soup mixture and cooked rice to the beef mixture. Stir and bring to a simmer over medium heat. Reduce the heat to low and cook, stirring occasionally, about 15 minutes, or until the sauce is lightly thickened and the flavors are blended. Sprinkle with the mozzarella and serve.

Makes 6 servings

Per serving: *350 calories, 30 g protein, 36 g carbohydrate, 8 g fat, 75 mg cholesterol, 200 mg sodium, 1 g fiber*

Diet Exchanges: *0 milk, 2 vegetable, 0 fruit, 1½ bread, 4 meat, 1 fat*

2½ Carb Choices

350 Calories

Swiss Steak

—Lonnie McDonald, Sellersville, Pennsylvania

Round steak can be especially tough unless it's cooked slowly—this amazing sauce renders the beef fork-tender.

Prep time: 15 minutes
Cook time: 6 minutes
Bake time: 2 hours

¼ cup all-purpose flour

1 teaspoon mustard powder

½ teaspoon salt

1¼ pounds lean, boneless beef top round steak (½" thick)

1 teaspoon olive oil

1 pound plum tomatoes, chopped

1 medium onion, sliced

2 carrots, chopped

1 tablespoon Worcestershire sauce

2 tablespoons brown sugar

Preheat the oven to 325°F. In a small bowl, combine the flour, mustard, and salt. Rub the mixture on both sides of the steak. Discard any remaining flour mixture.

In a large nonstick skillet over medium-high heat, warm the oil. Add the steak and cook, turning once, until browned.

Transfer the steak to a 13" × 9" baking dish, and top with the tomatoes, onion, and carrots. Drizzle with the Worcestershire sauce, and sprinkle with the brown sugar. Cover with foil and bake for 2 hours, or until the steak is fork-tender. Cut the steak into four pieces and serve with the vegetables and pan juices.

Makes 4 servings

Per serving: *350 calories, 34 g protein, 22 g carbohydrate, 14 g fat, 60 mg cholesterol, 450 mg sodium, 3 g fiber*

Diet Exchanges: *0 milk, 2 vegetable, 0 fruit, 1 bread, 4½ meat, 2 fat*

1½ Carb Choices

260 Calories

Spaghetti Pie

—Elena Martlock, Bethlehem, Pennsylvania

This dish is a great way to use leftover pasta—but it's so tasty you might just want to make the whole thing from scratch anyway.

Prep time: 15 minutes
Cook time: 11 minutes
Bake time: 40 minutes

½ **pound whole wheat spaghetti**

½ **pound 95% lean ground beef**

2 **cups marinara sauce**

1 **cup part-skim ricotta cheese or 1% cottage cheese**

¾ **cup shredded part-skim mozzarella cheese**

3 **tablespoons grated Parmesan cheese**

¼ **teaspoon salt**

¼ **teaspoon ground black pepper**

2 **large eggs, well beaten**

Preheat the oven to 350°F. Coat a round, 9" to 10" deep pie plate dish with olive oil spray.

Cook the pasta according to the package directions. Drain the pasta and return to the cooking pot.

Meanwhile, in a large, deep nonstick skillet over medium-high heat, cook the ground beef, breaking it up with the back of a wooden spoon, about 7 minutes, or until no longer pink. Drain in a colander. In a medium bowl, combine the beef and marinara sauce.

Stir the ricotta or cottage cheese, ½ cup mozzarella, Parmesan, salt, and pepper into the pasta. Stir in the eggs.

Layer one-half of the pasta mixture in the prepared pie plate and cover with one-half of the meat sauce. Repeat with the remaining pasta mixture and meat sauce. Cover with foil and bake 20 minutes. Uncover and bake 10 minutes. Sprinkle with the remaining ¼ cup mozzarella and bake 10 minutes longer, or until the cheese has melted and the pie is set and firm. Cut into wedges to serve.

Makes 8 servings

Per serving: *260 calories, 20 g protein, 27 g carbohydrate, 9 g fat, 90 mg cholesterol, 540 mg sodium, 4 g fiber*

Diet Exchanges: *0 milk, 0 vegetable, 0 fruit, 0 bread, 2 meat, 1 fat*

2 Carb Choices

490 Calories

Beef Stroganoff

—Chris Detris, Breinigsville, Pennsylvania

*This classic dish is considerably lighter when you use reduced-fat ingredients—
best of all, it's just as delicious!*

Prep time: 10 minutes
Cook time: 55 minutes

  1 tablespoon olive oil
 12 ounces boneless beef top round, cut into 1" cubes
 ½ cup chopped onion
    Salt
    Ground black pepper
  2 cups reduced-sodium beef broth, plus more if necessary
  1 tablespoon Worcestershire sauce
  1 can (4 ounces) sliced mushrooms, undrained, or 2 cups sliced fresh mushrooms
 ½ pound wide whole wheat blend egg noodles
  1 cup fat-free sour cream
  2 tablespoons all-purpose flour

In a large nonstick skillet over medium-high heat, warm the oil. Add the beef and onion, and cook, stirring occasionally, about 10 minutes, or until the beef is lightly browned. Season to taste with salt and pepper.

Add the broth and Worcestershire sauce; bring to a boil. Reduce the heat to low, cover, and simmer, stirring occasionally, for 25 minutes. Add the canned mushrooms (and their juices) or the fresh mushrooms; cover and simmer about 20 minutes longer, or until the beef is fork-tender.

Meanwhile, cook the noodles according to the package directions and drain. Return the noodles to the cooking pot and cover to keep warm.

In a small bowl, whisk the sour cream and flour. Stir in to the bubbling stew and cook, stirring, about 5 minutes, or until thickened. Add more broth if the sauce becomes too thick. Serve the stroganoff over the noodles.

Makes 4 servings

Per serving: *490 calories, 31 g protein, 59 g carbohydrate, 15 g fat, 55 mg cholesterol, 410 mg sodium, 4 g fiber*

Diet Exchanges: *0 milk, 1 vegetable, 0 fruit, 0 bread, 3 meat, 1½ fat*

4 Carb Choices

260 Calories

Teriyaki Steak Strips
—Kathy Schuessler, Emmaus, Pennsylvania

Cooking flank steak or top round just to medium rare and slicing it thinly will ensure tenderness and juiciness.

Prep time: 5 minutes
Marinate time: 8 hours
Grill time: 10 to 14 minutes

¼ **cup vegetable oil**
⅓ **cup reduced-sodium soy sauce**
2 **tablespoons dry sherry**
3 **cloves garlic, minced**
3 **tablespoons brown sugar**
1½ **pounds boneless beef flank steak or top round steak**

In a shallow dish, combine the oil, soy sauce, sherry, garlic, and brown sugar. Add the steak, turning to coat. Cover and marinate in the refrigerator 6 to 8 hours, turning the steak once or twice.

Heat a barbecue grill to medium-hot, or preheat the broiler and coat a broiler-pan rack with cooking spray. Remove the steak from the marinade. Discard the marinade. Grill or broil the steak 5 to 7 minutes per side for medium rare, or to desired doneness. Slice the steak diagonally across the grain and serve.

Makes 6 servings

Per serving: *260 calories, 25 g protein, 6 g carbohydrate, 14 g fat, 45 mg cholesterol, 600 mg sodium, 0 g fiber*

Diet Exchanges: *0 milk, 0 vegetable, 0 fruit, ½ bread, 3½ meat, 1 fat*

½ **Carb Choice**

SHOPPING SAVVY

Whole Wheat Orzo

RiceSelect's new Whole Wheat Orzo packs a lot of nutrition into a tiny rice-shaped piece of pasta. Each 2-ounce (dry) serving offers 9 grams of wholesome fiber. Up the fiber and flavor by stirring frozen peas, canned beans, fresh spinach, or Steamed Lentils (see Shopping Savvy, page 126) into the cooking orzo about 1 minute before draining. Then toss with a touch of fruity olive oil and Parmesan.

RiceSelect also produces Whole Grain Royal Blends. These mixes combine delicious, fiber-full grains such as Texmati brown rice, wild rice, red rice, wheat berries, barley, and rye. Also check out their organic whole wheat couscous. Sold in 32-ounce tubs, RiceSelect products are available in many supermarkets, including Whole Foods. Or go to www.riceselect.com.

Pammy's Curry in a Hurry!

—Pamela Lebi, Tucson, Arizona

"This recipe is so flavorful and tasty! The herbs and meat really fill me up—a little bit goes a long way. I prepare the meal so quickly I have time to exercise!"

Prep time: 15 minutes
Cook time: 13 minutes

1 **pound pork tenderloin, trimmed, cut into 1"-thick slices, each slice halved or cut into strips**

2 **teaspoons sweet curry powder**
  Salt
  Ground black pepper

2 **tablespoons olive oil**

1 **medium onion, chopped**

3 **cloves garlic, minced**
  Large pinch ground red pepper

1 **can (8 ounces) tomato sauce**

½ **cup reduced-sodium, fat-free chicken or vegetable broth**

2 **tablespoons no-salt-added tomato paste**

2 **cups frozen wax beans or Italian cut green beans**

1½ **cups hot cooked brown rice**

Toss the pork with ½ teaspoon curry powder and salt and black pepper to taste. In a large nonstick skillet over medium-high heat, warm the oil. Add the pork and cook, stirring, 3 to 5 minutes, or until lightly browned. Transfer to a medium bowl.

Add the onion and garlic to the skillet, and cook, stirring often, about 4 minutes, or until tender. Add the remaining 1½ teaspoons curry powder and the ground red pepper. Cook, stirring, for 1 minute. Stir in the tomato sauce, broth, and tomato paste. Bring to a boil. Return the pork and any juices to the skillet. Stir in the wax beans. Bring to a simmer. Reduce the heat to low, cover, and simmer 5 to 7 minutes, or until the pork is tender and the vegetables are heated through. Serve over the rice.

Makes 4 servings

Per serving: *340 calories, 29 g protein, 31 g carbohydrate, 12 g fat, 75 mg cholesterol, 420 mg sodium, 5 g fiber*

Diet Exchanges: *0 milk, 2½ vegetable, 0 fruit, 1 bread, 3½ meat, 2 fat*

2 Carb Choices

410 Calories

Garlic Pork

—Lonnie McDonald, Sellersville, Pennsylvania

Prep time: 15 minutes
Marinate time: 15 minutes
Cook time: 22 minutes

  2 tablespoons cornstarch
  2 tablespoons reduced-sodium soy sauce
  1 tablespoon dry sherry
  2 large cloves garlic, minced
  ¾ pound pork tenderloin, trimmed and cut into ½" cubes
  ½ pound Udon noodles
  2 tablespoons olive oil
  ¾ cup fat-free, reduced-sodium chicken broth
  1 package (1 pound) frozen mixed broccoli, carrots, water chestnuts, and red peppers
  2 tablespoons chopped peanuts
  2 tablespoons chopped scallion

Combine the cornstarch, soy sauce, sherry, and garlic in a medium bowl. Add the pork, toss to mix well, cover, and marinate 15 minutes.

Meanwhile, prepare the Udon noodles according to package directions. Drain. Transfer to a serving bowl and cover to keep warm.

In large skillet or wok over medium-high heat, warm the oil. With a slotted spoon, transfer the pork from the marinade to the skillet. Cook, stirring frequently, for 5 to 7 minutes, or until the pork is browned. Add the broth and remaining marinade and bring to a boil, stirring. Add the vegetables and cook, stirring often, for 3 to 5 minutes, or until thickened and heated through. Spoon over the cooked noodles and sprinkle with the peanuts and scallion.

Makes 4 servings

Per serving: *410 calories, 25 g protein, 45 g carbohydrate, 12 g fat, 55 mg cholesterol, 810 mg sodium, 3 g fiber*

Diet Exchanges: *0 milk, 1½ vegetable, 0 fruit, 2½ bread, 3 meat, 2 fat*

3 Carb Choices

Breads, Breakfasts, Drinks, and Desserts

BREADS

BREAKFASTS

DRINKS

DESSERTS

230 Calories

Ricebread

—Steve Stanford, Smithville, Mississippi

This treat is not only healthy, but slightly sweet!

Prep time: 10 minutes
Bake time: 20 minutes

  2 **cups brown rice flour**
  1 **tablespoon granulated sugar**
  2 **teaspoons baking powder**
½ **teaspoon salt**
1¼ **cups 2% milk**
  2 **large eggs**
  3 **tablespoons olive oil**

Preheat the oven to 425°F. Lightly oil a 9" cast-iron skillet. While you prepare the batter, heat the skillet in the oven for 5 minutes, or until very hot. (If it's not hot, the bread will stick.)

In a large bowl, stir together the rice flour, sugar, baking powder, and salt. Measure the milk in a 2-cup glass measure. Add the eggs and the oil to the milk, and beat with a fork until well blended.

Pour the milk mixture over the dry ingredients, and stir just until blended. Pour the batter into the hot skillet. Bake 20 to 25 minutes, or until brown and firm. Serve warm.

Makes 8 servings

Per serving: *230 calories, 6 g protein, 34 g carbohydrate, 8 g fat, 55 mg cholesterol, 310 mg sodium, 2 g fiber*

Diet Exchanges: *0 milk, 0 vegetable, 0 fruit, 2 bread, 0 meat, 1½ fat*

2 Carb Choices

Oatmeal-Apple Scones

—Cecilia Haberzettl, Pottstown, Pennsylvania

Prep time: 15 minutes
Bake time: 25 minutes

1½ cups all-purpose flour
1 cup old-fashioned or quick oats
2 teaspoons baking powder
½ teaspoon baking soda
¼ teaspoon salt
½ cup cold trans-free margarine, cut into small pieces
2 large egg whites
¼ cup packed light brown sugar
¼ cup fat-free milk
1 tablespoon molasses
1 teaspoon orange extract
1 medium apple, peeled, cored, and coarsely chopped
½ cup dark raisins

Preheat the oven to 350°F. Coat a baking sheet with cooking spray.

In a large bowl, stir together the flour, oats, baking powder, baking soda, and salt. Cut in the margarine with a pastry blender or two knives until the mixture forms coarse crumbs.

In a medium bowl, whisk together the egg whites, brown sugar, milk, molasses, and orange extract until well blended. Add the milk mixture to the dry ingredients, and stir until a sticky dough forms. Stir in the apple and raisins. Knead in the bowl just until well blended.

On the prepared baking sheet, pat the dough into an 8" circle. Cut into 8 wedges. Spread the wedges apart slightly. Bake for about 25 minutes, or until browned and a wooden pick inserted in the center of a scone comes out clean.

Cool on a wire rack for 10 minutes before serving.

Makes 8

Per serving: *280 calories, 5 g protein, 43 g carbohydrate, 10 g fat, 0 mg cholesterol, 390 mg sodium, 2 g fiber*

Diet Exchanges: *0 milk, 0 vegetable, ½ fruit, 2 bread, 0 meat, 2 fat*

3 Carb Choices

130 Calories

Carrot Muffins

—Tiwanna Capochichi, Brooklyn, New York

Prep time: 15 minutes
Bake time: 25 minutes

1 cup whole wheat flour
½ cup oat bran
1 teaspoon baking powder
1 teaspoon baking soda
1 teaspoon ground cinnamon
½ teaspoon ground allspice
¼ teaspoon salt
⅔ cup grated carrots
½ cup golden raisins
⅓ cup maple syrup
¼ cup water
¼ cup canola oil

Preheat the oven to 375°F. Line a 12-cup muffin pan with paper or foil liners.

In a large bowl, stir together the whole wheat flour, oat bran, baking powder, baking soda, cinnamon, allspice, and salt. Stir in the carrots and raisins. Add the maple syrup, water, and oil, and stir to mix well.

Spoon the batter evenly into the lined muffin cups. Bake for 25 to 30 minutes, or until the muffins are golden and a toothpick inserted in the center of a muffin comes out clean. Turn muffins out of the pan onto a rack. Cool for 10 minutes before serving.

Makes 12

Per serving: *130 calories, 2 g protein, 22 g carbohydrate, 5 g fat, 0 mg cholesterol, 200 mg sodium, 3 g fiber*

Diet Exchanges: *0 milk, 0 vegetable, ½ fruit, 1 bread, 0 meat, 1 fat*

1½ Carb Choices

180 Calories

Raisin Bran Muffins

—Julie Nusbaum, Hamilton, Indiana

"Because the batter can be stored so long, it's easy to maintain portion control by only making the number of muffins you need at a time."

Prep time: 10 minutes
Chill time: Overnight
Bake time: 15 minutes

1½ cups all-purpose flour
1 cup whole wheat flour
2½ teaspoons baking soda
2 teaspoons ground cinnamon
1 teaspoon ground nutmeg
1 teaspoon salt
2 large eggs
1½ cups sugar
½ cup canola oil
2 cups buttermilk
3¾ box Raisin Bran cereal (7½ ounces)

In a large bowl, stir together the all-purpose flour, whole wheat flour, baking soda, cinnamon, nutmeg, and salt.

In another large bowl, with a wire whisk, lightly beat the eggs. Beat in the sugar, then the oil, and finally the buttermilk.

Add the buttermilk mixture to the dry ingredients and stir until well blended. Stir in the cereal. Pour into a large container. Cover and refrigerate overnight or up to 6 weeks.

To bake the muffins, preheat the oven to 400°F. Line a 12-cup muffin pan with paper or foil liners. (If baking just a few muffins at a time, place foil liners directly on a baking sheet.) Spoon the batter into the lined muffin cups, filling them two-thirds full (about ¼ cup). Bake for 15 to 20 minutes, or until browned and firm to the touch. Turn the muffins out of the pan onto a rack to cool.

Makes 24

Per serving: *180 calories, 3 g protein, 31 g carbohydrate, 6 g fat, 0 mg cholesterol, 310 mg sodium, 2 g fiber*

Diet Exchanges: *0 milk, 0 vegetable, 0 fruit, 2 bread, 0 meat, 1 fat*

2 Carb Choices

300
Calories

Morning Starter

—Kim Crump, Sacramento, California

*"This easy dish has cured my taste for sweets in the morning. No pastry for me.
I find myself fulfilled until lunchtime."*

Prep time: 5 minutes

- ½ **cup plain fat-free yogurt**
- 1 **small banana, sliced**
- ½ **cup low-fat granola with almonds and raisins**

In a bowl, mix the yogurt, banana, and granola.

Makes 1 serving

Per serving: *300 calories, 9 g protein, 65 g carbohydrate, 2 g fat, 5 mg cholesterol, 220 mg sodium, 5 g fiber*

Diet Exchanges: *½ milk, 0 vegetable, 1½ fruit, 2 bread, 0 meat, 0 fat*

4 Carb Choices

SHOPPING SAVVY

Great Grains!

Pepperidge Farm has two new great-tasting breads made with 100% stone-ground whole wheat flour. Check out Cinnamon Whole Grain Swirl Bread and Cinnamon and Raisins Whole Grain Swirl Bread. One delicious slice adds 2 grams of fiber to your daily total. English muffin lovers will want to try Pepperidge Farm's new 7-Grain English Muffins. They're a bit higher in calories (130 vs. 110 for the bread) but they provide 3 grams of fiber as well. Look for these products in the bread aisles of your local supermarkets.

Peach Breakfast Parfait

—Stephanie Little, Cypress, Texas

"This recipe is so easy and it tastes so great."

Prep time: 5 minutes

- 1 cup canned peach slices (water or juice-packed), drained
- 1 cup fat-free vanilla yogurt
- ½ cup low-fat granola
- Ground cinnamon

Divide the peaches between 2 cereal bowls, and spoon the yogurt on top. Top with the granola, and sprinkle with cinnamon to taste.

Makes 2 servings

Per serving: *250 calories, 8 g protein, 52 g carbohydrate, 1 g fat, 5 mg cholesterol, 150 mg sodium, 3 g fiber*

Diet Exchanges: *0 milk, 0 vegetable, 1 fruit, 2½ bread, 0 meat, 0 fat*

3½ Carb Choices

310
Calories

Chocolate Oatmeal

—Mary LaSee, Naples, Florida

"This recipe gives me the goodness of oatmeal and the thrill of chocolate for breakfast. It's very satisfying and nutritious. Serve with fat-free milk."

Prep time: 5 minutes
Microwave time: 6 minutes

    1 cup old-fashioned oats
    2 cups water
    2 tablespoons freshly ground flaxseed
    2 tablespoons unsweetened cocoa powder
    4 teaspoons Splenda or sugar
    ¼ cup chopped walnuts

Place the oats and water in large microwaveable bowl or container. Cover loosely with a lid or vented plastic wrap and microwave on high, stirring once or twice, for 6 minutes, or until the oats are softened. Mix in the flaxseed, cocoa, and Splenda or sugar until well blended. Spoon into 2 bowls, and sprinkle evenly with the walnuts.

Makes 2 servings

Per serving: *310 calories, 12 g protein, 35 g carbohydrate, 16 g fat, 0 mg cholesterol, 5 mg sodium, 8 g fiber*

Diet Exchanges: *0 milk, 0 vegetable, 0 fruit, 2 bread, ½ meat, 3 fat*

2 Carb Choices

400 Calories

Quick Grits and "Sausage"

—Jeffrey Gardner, Whiteville, North Carolina

"This delicious, quick, low-fat breakfast rivals anything on the breakfast menu at those all-too-tempting fast-food places."

Prep time: 5 minutes
Microwave time: 3 minutes

3 tablespoons instant grits
2 patties fully cooked vegetarian breakfast sausage, thawed (if frozen) and
   crumbled
¾ cup fat-free milk
   Salt
   Ground black pepper
   Tabasco sauce (optional)
1 slice Kraft 2% Milk Cheddar cheese

In a large microwaveable bowl, combine the grits, sausage, and milk. Cover loosely with a lid or vented plastic wrap and microwave on high for 2½ to 3 minutes, stirring once halfway through, until hot and bubbly. Season to taste with salt, pepper, and Tabasco (if using). Top with the cheese. Cover and microwave on high 30 seconds longer, or until the cheese is melted.

Makes 1 serving

Per serving: *400 calories, 35 g protein, 40 g carbohydrate, 11 g fat, 20 mg cholesterol, 100 mg sodium, 2 g fiber*

Diet Exchanges: *1 milk, 0 vegetable, 0 fruit, 1½ bread, 1 meat, ½ fat*

3 Carb Choices

Sausage and Egg Overnight Casserole

—Lonnie McDonald, Sellersville, Pennsylvania

Prep time: 10 minutes
Chill time: Overnight
Bake time: 35 minutes

  2 teaspoons olive oil
  1 large onion, chopped
  1 pound lean turkey sausage, casings removed
  1½ cups fat-free egg substitute
  6 large eggs
  2 cups fat-free milk
  ½ teaspoon mustard powder
  2 cups cubed whole grain bread
  1 can (8 ounces) kernel corn, drained
  ½ cup shredded Cheddar or Monterey Jack cheese

In a large skillet over medium-high heat, warm the oil. Add the onion and cook, stirring frequently, 5 minutes, or until softened and lightly browned. Add the sausage and cook, breaking up the sausage with the back of a spoon, 10 minutes, or until no longer pink.

In a large bowl, whisk the egg substitute, eggs, milk, and mustard. In a 13" × 9" baking dish, layer the bread cubes, sausage mixture, and corn. Pour the egg mixture over the top. Cover and refrigerate overnight.

The next day, preheat the oven to 350°F. Sprinkle the top of the casserole with the cheese. Bake uncovered for 35 to 45 minutes, or until eggs are set. Cut into squares and serve.

Makes 10 servings

Per serving: *210 calories, 21 g protein, 13 g carbohydrate, 8 g fat, 145 mg cholesterol, 250 mg sodium, 1 g fiber*

Diet Exchanges: *0 milk, ½ vegetable, ½ fruit, ½ bread, 1 meat, ½ fat*

1 Carb Choice

200 Calories

Sausage Gravy and Biscuits

—Sally Waggoner, Muncie, Indiana

"My kids love this classic Midwestern breakfast on the weekend. By using lower-fat ingredients, I can slash calories without sacrificing taste."

Prep time: 15 minutes
Bake time: 10 minutes
Cook time: 25 minutes

B I S C U I T S

1½ **cups reduced-fat biscuit mix**
½ **cup fat-free milk**

G R A V Y

½ **pound turkey breakfast sausage, casings removed**
3 **cups fat-free milk**
¼ **cup all-purpose flour**
⅛ **teaspoon salt**
¼ **teaspoon ground black pepper, or to taste**

To make the biscuits: Preheat the oven to 450°F. Coat a baking sheet with cooking spray. In a large bowl, combine the biscuit mix and milk, mixing until a soft dough forms. Turn out onto a floured work surface and roll into a circle about ½" thick using a lightly floured rolling pin. With a floured 2½" biscuit cutter, cut out 8 rounds. Place on prepared baking sheet. Bake 8 to 10 minutes, or until lightly browned. Transfer biscuits to a cooling rack.

To make the gravy: In a large nonstick skillet, cook the sausage over medium heat, breaking it up with the back of a wooden spoon, for about 5 minutes, or until no longer pink. Transfer the sausage to a bowl and cover to keep warm.

In a medium bowl, whisk together the milk, flour, salt, and pepper just until the flour is dissolved. Add the mixture to the same skillet. Bring to a boil over medium heat, stirring often. Reduce the heat and simmer, stirring occasionally, for about 15 minutes, or until thickened. Add the reserved sausage and heat through. Serve the gravy over split biscuits.

Makes 8 servings

Per serving: *200 calories, 12 g protein, 24 g carbohydrate, 6 g fat, 25 mg cholesterol, 540 mg sodium, 0 g fiber*

Diet Exchanges: *½ milk, 0 vegetable, 0 fruit, 1 bread, 1 meat, ½ fat*

2 Carb Choices

260 Calories

Easy Asparagus Omelet

—Lynn Phillips, Macungie, Pennsylvania

Prep time: 5 minutes
Cook time: 10 minutes

　3　large eggs

　4　large egg whites

　3　tablespoons 1% milk

　　　Salt

　　　Ground black pepper

　2　tablespoons trans-free margarine

⅓　cup shredded, reduced-fat Cheddar cheese

　1　cup steamed asparagus tips

Preheat the broiler. In a medium bowl, beat the eggs, egg whites, and milk. Season to taste with salt and pepper.

Melt the margarine in a medium nonstick oven-proof skillet over medium-high heat. (If the skillet isn't oven-proof, wrap the handle in heavy-duty foil.) Cook until beginning to brown. Add the egg mixture and cook, stirring lightly with a fork, until it begins to thicken, 15 to 20 seconds. Cook, gently lifting edges to allow uncooked egg to run underneath, until half the egg mixture is set, about 6 to 8 minutes.

Remove from the heat and sprinkle with the cheese. Top with asparagus tips. Broil 4" from the heat for about 1 to 2 minutes, or until the cheese is melted and the omelet is puffy and set. Slide omelet onto serving plate and cut in half to serve.

Makes 2 servings

Per serving: *260 calories, 26 g protein, 9 g carbohydrate, 15 g fat, 340 mg cholesterol, 257 mg sodium, 3 g fiber*

Diet Exchanges: *0 milk, 1 vegetable, 0 fruit, 0 bread, 2 meat, 2 fat*

½ **Carb Choice**

100 Calories

Breakfast Eggs

—Dawn Hurtado, Vandalia, Illinois

Prep time: 5 minutes
Cook time: 4 minutes

½ **cup egg substitute**
   Salt
   Ground black pepper
2 **tablespoons light cream cheese, cut into small pieces**

Mix the egg substitute with salt and pepper to taste. Coat a small nonstick skillet with olive oil spray, and heat over medium-low heat. Pour the eggs into the skillet and cook, stirring a few times, until almost set. Gently fold in the cream cheese. Cook for 1 minute longer. Remove the skillet from the heat, cover, and let stand until the cream cheese has melted.

Makes 1 serving

Per serving: *100 calories, 15 g protein, 3 g carbohydrate, 2.5 g fat, 10 mg cholesterol, 340 mg sodium, 0 g fiber*

Diet Exchanges: *0 milk, 0 vegetable, 0 fruit, 0 bread, ½ meat, ½ fat*

0 Carb Choices

···· SECRETS OF WEIGHT-LOSS WINNERS ····

• Put your stationary bike in front of the TV and watch your favorite shows while doing something for your mind and body.

—Mary Meissner, Pueblo, Colorado

• Always eat breakfast. Try to eat a low-fat cereal with some protein and high fiber. It will keep you feeling full longer and keep you from wanting to snack before lunch.

—Julie Lee, San Francisco, California

260 Calories

Easy Egg Wraps

—Paula Saulnier, Midlothian, Virginia

"This is a weekend dish I love to make for myself and family. It feels like a high-fat dish because it's so tasty, but it isn't!"

Prep time: 5 minutes
Cook time: 9 minutes

⅓ cup chopped sweet white onion or scallion

¼ cup chopped red bell pepper

1 cup egg substitute

  Salt

  Ground black pepper

⅓ cup shredded reduced-fat cheese of your choice

2 whole wheat soft taco wraps (8" in diameter), heated according to package directions

¼ cup salsa

Coat a medium nonstick skillet with cooking spray and heat over medium heat. Add the onion or scallion and bell pepper. Cook, stirring often, 5 minutes, or until tender. Pour in the egg substitute, and season to taste with salt and pepper. Cook, stirring often, until the eggs are almost set.

Remove the skillet from the heat and sprinkle with the cheese. Cover and let stand for 1 minute, or until the cheese has melted. Spoon the egg mixture onto the warmed wraps, and top with the salsa. Roll up the wraps, folding in the sides.

Makes 2 servings

Per serving: *260 calories, 22 g protein, 33 g carbohydrate, 7 g fat, 15 mg cholesterol, 900 mg sodium, 9 g fiber*

Diet Exchanges: *0 milk, ½ vegetable, 0 fruit, 0 bread, 1 meat, ½ fat*

2 Carb Choices

180 Calories

Rock-You Shake

—Dana Bland, Richmond, Virginia

"Since March of 2001, I have lost over 100 pounds and have kept the weight off by creating fun shakes and healthy smoothies! I love to have this after an intense workout. It cools me down and makes me feel refreshed and completely satisfied and energized."

Prep time: 5 minutes

 1 cup fat-free milk or soy milk
 1 envelope (¾ ounce) **Alba Chocolate Fit & Frosty Shake Mix**
 1 tablespoon unsweetened cocoa powder
 2 tablespoons peanut butter
 1½ cups ice

In a blender, combine the milk, shake mix, and cocoa, and process to mix well. Add the peanut butter and ice; process until smooth and frosty.

Makes 2 servings

Per serving: *180 calories, 12 g protein, 17 g carbohydrate, 9 g fat, 5 mg cholesterol, 190 mg sodium, 3 g fiber*

Diet Exchanges: *½ milk, 0 vegetable, 0 fruit, 0 bread, ½ meat, 1½ fat*

1 Carb Choice

···· SECRETS OF WEIGHT-LOSS WINNERS ····

• If you're really craving something in particular, you might as well just go ahead and have a small portion of it, because nothing else will satisfy that craving. The big picture is that you'll be able to stay on your diet longer.

—Kathy Nornick, Harrisonburg, Virginia

• When I go shopping for groceries, I pick up five 5-pound bags of sugar and

hold them for a minute. That is the 25 pounds I have lost. Holding the bags and feeling the weight makes me proud of myself and motivates me to buy healthy food.

—Nancy Gruzleski, Uniontown, Ohio

Good Morning Shake

230 Calories

—Anna Allison, Muncy, Pennsylvania

"This recipe gives me energy for the entire morning, has fiber, and is very low-fat. It helps me to feel full so I don't have to munch at anything in the office (or elsewhere), plus it is very quick and easy to make."

Prep time: 10 minutes

1½ cups fat-free milk

½ apple, peeled and cored

1 slice peeled, seeded papaya or ½ banana

1 tablespoon quick-cooking oats

½ teaspoon vanilla extract

5 to 6 ice cubes

In a blender, combine the milk, apple, papaya or banana, oats, vanilla, and ice. Process until smooth and frosty.

Makes 1 serving

Per serving: *230 calories, 15 g protein, 42 g carbohydrate, 0.5 g fat, 5 mg cholesterol, 200 mg sodium, 4 g fiber*

Diet Exchanges: *1½ milk, 0 vegetable, 1 fruit, 0 bread, 0 meat, 0 fat*

3 Carb Choices

120 Calories

"Wake Up and Sing" Drink

—Margaly Patterson, Miami, Florida

"Grapefruit makes me feel lighter and makes a satisfying drink!"

Prep time: 5 minutes

2 teaspoons grated peeled fresh ginger
½ cup tap water or sparkling water
1 cup pink or red grapefruit juice
1 teaspoon sugar or Splenda
½ teaspoon vanilla extract (optional)
  Ice cubes
  Strawberries or orange slices, for garnish (optional)

In a blender, combine the ginger and water, and puree. Strain the mixture through a sieve into a bowl. Add the grapefruit juice, sugar or Splenda, and vanilla extract (if using). Serve over ice. Garnish with strawberries or orange slices, if you like.

Makes 1 serving

Per serving: *120 calories, 1 g protein, 28 g carbohydrate, 0 g fat, 0 mg cholesterol, 5 mg sodium, 0 g fiber*

Diet Exchanges: *0 milk, 0 vegetable, 1½ fruit, 0 bread, 0 meat, 0 fat*

2 Carb Choices

230 Calories

Breakfast Berry Smoothie

—Susan McClure, Edmonton, Alberta, Canada

"This smoothie has helped me control my appetite and makes breakfast a more enjoyable meal. Rather than skipping breakfast, I now enjoy this drink while watching the sun come up over the horizon in the early morning."

Prep time: 5 minutes

1 banana, cut into chunks

½ cup fat-free milk (cold in the summer, warm in the winter)

¼ cup frozen unsweetened blueberries

¼ cup frozen unsweetened strawberries

1 teaspoon peanut butter

½ teaspoon honey

In a blender, combine the banana, milk, blueberries, strawberries, peanut butter, and honey. Process about 1 minute, or until the consistency of a thick milkshake.

Makes 1 serving

Per serving: *230 calories, 7 g protein, 46 g carbohydrate, 3.5 g fat, 0 mg cholesterol, 90 mg sodium, 5 g fiber*

Diet Exchanges: *½ milk, 0 vegetable, 2½ fruit, 0 bread, 0 meat, ½ fat*

3 Carb Choices

Breakfast Smoothie

—Lori Lovesky, Sarasota, Florida

"This breakfast helped me lose the last of my 'baby weight' after my youngest child was born. I've kept drinking it because it's so healthy and tastes so good!"

Prep time: 5 minutes

- ¾ **cup fat-free vanilla yogurt**
- ½ **cup frozen unsweetened mixed berries**
- 1 **cup low-fat soy milk**
- 2 **tablespoons wheat germ**
- 1 **tablespoon flaxseed oil**

In a blender, combine the yogurt, berries, soy milk, wheat germ, and flaxseed oil. Process until smooth and frosty.

Makes 2 servings

Per serving: *230 calories, 8 g protein, 30 g carbohydrate, 8 g fat, 0 mg cholesterol, 95 mg sodium, 4 g fiber*

Diet Exchanges: *½ milk, 0 vegetable, ½ fruit, 1 bread, 0 meat, 1½ fat*

2 Carb Choices

SHOPPING SAVVY

Smoothie, Anyone?

Craving a smoothie? Don't drag out the container blender. Reach instead for Cuisinart's new Smart Stick Hand Blender. Simply place all ingredients in the dishwasher-safe beaker, insert the blender, press the button, and blend, using an up-and-down motion. To clean, snap off the stainless-steel shaft and rinse it or run it through the dishwasher.

Here's our easy smoothie for one: In the beaker, blend a 6-ounce container plain fat-free yogurt, 1 cup unsweetened frozen berries or sliced fruit (thawed slightly), and 1 tablespoon sugar. Cuisinart Smart Stick Hand Blender comes in red, white, and nifty brushed chrome. Sold in housewares stores.

Front, Milky Shake (opposite page)
and *Back,* Rock-You Shake (page 210)

380 Calories

Milky Shake

—Sothchith Chea, Lancaster, Pennsylvania

Prep time: 5 minutes

1½ cups fat-free milk

¼ cup fat-free French vanilla–flavored nondairy creamer

1 to 2 tablespoons peanut butter

1 teaspoon ground flaxseed

1 teaspoon sesame seeds, toasted if you like

1 cup ice cubes

In a blender, combine the milk, creamer, peanut butter, flaxseed, sesame seeds, and ice. Process until the ice is crushed.

Makes 1 serving

Per serving: *380 calories, 18 g protein, 52 g carbohydrate, 10 g fat, 5 mg cholesterol, 290 mg sodium, 2 g fiber*

Diet Exchanges: *1½ milk, 0 vegetable, 0 fruit, 1½ bread, ½ meat, 2 fat*

3½ Carb Choices

SECRETS OF WEIGHT-LOSS WINNERS

• I am always tempted to eat as I cook dinner, sometimes eating almost as much as a normal dinner before I sit down and eat another dinner. I have learned to have many carrot sticks on hand. When I feel like putting something in my mouth, that's what it is.

I have lost 5 pounds in 2 months with this method.

—Kimberly Schmidt, Winnipeg, Manitoba, Canada

• To lose 5 pounds or so, stop drinking soda. Replace it with water and green tea.

—Kimberly Miller, Wilkinsburg, Pennsylvania

Strawberry Refresher

—Susan Skepper, Mesa, Arizona

Prep time: 5 minutes

2 cups frozen unsweetened strawberries
2 cups fat-free milk
4 packets (.035 ounce each) Splenda

In a blender, combine the strawberries, milk, and Splenda. Process until smooth and frosty.

Makes 2 servings

Per serving: *150 calories, 10 g protein, 28 g carbohydrate, 0 g fat, 5 mg cholesterol, 135 mg sodium, 3 g fiber*

Diet Exchanges: *1 milk, 0 vegetable, 1 fruit, 0 bread, 0 meat, 0 fat*

2 Carb Choices

160 Calories

Creamsicle Smoothie

—Kat Eicholtz, Sterling, Virginia

"Tastes decadently rich but is low-calorie and healthy."

Prep time: 5 minutes

- 1 navel orange, peeled
- ¼ cup fat-free half-and-half or fat-free yogurt
- 2 tablespoons frozen orange juice concentrate
- ¼ teaspoon vanilla extract
- 4 ice cubes

In a blender, combine the orange, half-and-half or yogurt, orange juice concentrate, vanilla, and ice cubes. Process until smooth.

Makes 1 serving

Per serving: *160 calories, 4 g protein, 37 g carbohydrate, 1 g fat, 5 mg cholesterol, 90 mg sodium, 3 g fiber*

Diet Exchanges: *0 milk, 0 vegetable, 2 fruit, 0 bread, 0 meat, 0 fat*

2½ Carb Choices

· · · SHOPPING SAVVY · · · · · · · · · · ·

Bake It Better

For scrumptious baked goods that are good for you, mostly, substitute King Arthur All-Natural White Whole Wheat Flour for some of the all-purpose flour. White whole wheat flour adds the good nutrients and fiber of regular whole wheat flour. But your family won't even know they're eating whole wheat because of the lighter color and milder flavor.

Here's how to use the white whole wheat flour: For breads using regular whole wheat flour, replace it cup for cup. For "craggy" cookies, such as hermits or oatmeal, exchange half the all-purpose flour with white whole wheat flour. Add a little water if the mixture seems drier. A King Arthur tip: "Let the baked cookies or bars rest for 24 hours, at room temperature, before serving. This rest gives the bran a chance to soften."

Look for white whole wheat flour in supermarkets or go to bakerscatalogue. com. Keep in the freezer or fridge so it stays fresh.

Fruity Yogurt

—Carolyn Jackson, Rochester, New York

"When I start my day with a fruity yogurt, I get a wonderful burst of energy that lasts, without the need to snack later on."

Prep time: 5 minutes

1 banana, peeled
1 cup chopped fresh fruit in season
¼ cup orange juice, preferably fresh-squeezed
¼ cup plain low-fat yogurt
2 tablespoons honey
5 to 6 small ice cubes

In a blender, combine the banana, fruit, orange juice, yogurt, honey, and ice. Process until smooth.

Makes 1 serving

Per serving: *380 calories, 6 g protein, 93 g carbohydrate, 2 g fat, 5 mg cholesterol, 45 mg sodium, 7 g fiber*

Diet Exchanges: *½ milk, 0 vegetable, 4 fruit, 2 bread, 0 meat, 0 fat*

6 Carb Choices

SHOPPING SAVVY

Cool Treats

Indulge! Try Yoplait's new Frozen Yogurt & Cereal Bars. This is one frozen dessert that won't blow your diet. Rich in taste but low in calories and fat, the bars come in two great fruity flavors: Strawberry (120 calories) and Wildberry and Vanilla (110 calories). Packing as much calcium as an 8-ounce glass of milk, they've got a crisp cereal crust. Sold nationwide in boxes of four.

Great Low-Cal Oatmeal Cookies

80 Calories

—Judith Michalski, Rochester Hills, Michigan

"I crave sugar—by decreasing the sugar in these cookies I can still enjoy a sweet treat and lose weight. I store them in a plastic container and eat two cookies with a healthy meal."

Prep time: 15 minutes
Bake time: 10 minutes per batch

1½ cups all-purpose flour
 1 teaspoon ground cinnamon
 1 teaspoon baking soda
 ½ teaspoon salt
 3 cups old-fashioned or quick oats
 1 cup dark or golden raisins
 1 cup walnuts or pecans, finely chopped
 ½ cup reduced-calorie, trans-free margarine
 ¼ cup granulated sugar
 ¼ cup firmly packed brown sugar
 ¼ cup Splenda
 2 large eggs or ½ cup egg substitute
 ¾ cup unsweetened applesauce
 1 teaspoon vanilla extract

Preheat the oven to 350°F. Coat 2 or 3 heavy baking sheets with cooking spray.

In another large bowl, stir together the flour, cinnamon, baking soda, and salt. Stir in the oats, and then the raisins and nuts.

In another large bowl, with an electric mixer at medium speed, beat together the margarine, granulated and brown sugars, and Splenda until well blended. Beat in the eggs, one at a time, beating well after each (or beat in one-half of the egg substitute, followed by the other half). Beat in the applesauce and vanilla.

With mixer at low speed, add the dry ingredients, in 2 batches, just until blended. Drop the dough by heaping tablespoons onto the prepared baking sheets, spacing them 1" apart.

Bake until crisp and lightly brown, 10 to 12 minutes. Cool on sheet for 1 minute, then transfer cookies to racks to cool. Repeat with remaining dough.

Makes 4 dozen

Per cookie: *80 calories, 2 g protein, 12 g carbohydrate, 3.5 g fat, 10 mg cholesterol, 70 mg sodium, 1 g fiber*

Diet Exchanges: *0 milk, 0 vegetable, 0 fruit, ½ bread, 0 meat, ½ fat*

1 Carb Choice

Stained-Glass Cookies

—Cecilia Haberzettl, Pottstown, Pennsylvania

The tops of these pretty, colorful cookies are not hard to cut out. Choose a larger round cookie cutter and a smaller heart- or star-shaped cutter. The round shape is to cut out the "doughnut," and the smaller cutter is to cut out the doughnut's hole. Note: These are cookies for special occasions, but worth the time. Not too sweet and very attractive.

Prep time: 25 minutes
Chill time: 2 hours or up to overnight
Bake time: 10 minutes

  2 **cups all-purpose flour**
  ⅔ **cup reduced-calorie trans-free margarine**
  ½ **teaspoon almond extract**
  5 to 6 **tablespoons unsweetened apple juice or cranberry juice**
  ½ **cup jelly or fruit puree (any flavor)**

In a large bowl with a pastry blender or two knives, combine the flour, margarine, and almond extract. Add the juice, 1 tablespoon at a time, stirring, until a soft dough forms. Wrap the dough in plastic wrap and refrigerate until firm, 2 hours or overnight.

Preheat the oven to 350°F. Roll the dough to a ⅛" thickness. Cut into 2½" rounds with a large round cookie cutter. With a smaller cutter, cut out a heart or star in the center of half of the rounds. Remove each heart or star shape, leaving a hole in the center.

With a metal spatula, transfer the solid cookies and cutout shapes to cookie sheets and bake for about 10 minutes, or until just slightly golden. Cool the cookies on the sheets for 2 to 3 minutes. Place about ¼ teaspoon jelly in the center of each solid cookie (the jelly will melt slightly with the warmth of the cookie). Top each with a cutout cookie and press gently around the edges so the cookies stick together. Transfer to a wire rack and cool completely. Store the cookies between layers of plastic wrap in a cool place.

Makes 18

Per cookie: *130 calories, 1 g protein, 17 g carbohydrate, 6 g fat, 0 mg cholesterol, 55 mg sodium, 0 g fiber*

Diet Exchanges: *0 milk, 0 vegetable, 0 fruit, 1 bread, 0 meat, 0 fat*

1 Carb Choice

Raspberry-Oatmeal Squares

160 Calories

—Janet English, Toronto, Ontario, Canada

"This is a wonderful treat that satisfies one's sweet tooth; however, it is remarkably healthy at the same time!"

Prep time: 15 minutes
Bake time: 40 minutes

  2 **cups whole wheat pastry flour**
  ½ **cup old-fashioned oats**
  2 **tablespoons toasted wheat germ**
  ½ **cup packed brown sugar**
  1 **large egg, beaten**
  1 **teaspoon vanilla extract**
  ¾ **cup cold reduced-calorie, trans-free margarine**
  ¾ **cup sugar-free raspberry preserves**

Preheat the oven to 350°F. Coat an 8" × 8" baking pan with cooking spray.

In a large bowl, stir together the flour, oats, wheat germ, brown sugar, egg, and vanilla. Cut in the margarine with a pastry blender or two knives until the mixture forms coarse crumbs. Reserve 1½ cups of the mixture.

Press the remaining crumb mixture into the bottom of the prepared pan. Spread the preserves over the crust. Sprinkle the reserved crumbs evenly over the top.

Bake for 40 to 50 minutes, or until the crust is golden brown and crisp. Transfer to a wire rack to cool. Cut into squares.

Makes 16

Per square: *160 calories, 3 g protein, 22 g carbohydrate, 8 g fat, 0 mg cholesterol, 75 mg sodium, 2 g fiber*

Diet Exchanges: *0 milk, 0 vegetable, 0 fruit, 1 bread, 0 meat, 1½ fat*

1½ Carb Choices

170 Calories

Caramel Flan with Fresh Fruit

—David Purdy, Sacramento, California

Prep time: 20 minutes
Bake time: 20 minutes
Chill time: 24 hours

  ⅔ **cup sugar**
  1 **tablespoon water**
  3 **large eggs**
 1½ **cups 1% milk**
 1½ **teaspoons vanilla extract**
  2 **cups mixed raspberries, blackberries,
    and sliced kiwifruit**

Preheat the oven to 325°F.

In a heavy medium skillet over medium-high heat, combine ⅓ cup sugar and the water. Heat until the sugar is melted and caramelized (golden in color), stirring often. Carefully pour the caramelized sugar (it will be very hot) evenly into four or six 4- to 6-ounce ramekins or custard cups. Tilt the ramekins to coat the bottoms. Let stand for 10 minutes.

In a medium bowl, whisk the eggs and remaining ⅓ cup sugar until well blended.

Whisk in the milk and vanilla. Transfer the mixture to a large glass measuring cup or pitcher for easier handling. Pour evenly into the ramekins. Place the ramekins in a baking pan just large enough to hold them without touching. Place the pan on the oven rack and pour hot water into the pan to a depth of ½".

Bake the flans for 20 to 25 minutes, or until a knife inserted near the center comes out clean. Carefully lift the ramekins from the hot water onto a wire rack. Serve warm or cool completely, cover, and refrigerate for up to 24 hours. Garnish with the fresh fruit.

Makes 6 servings

Per serving: *170 calories, 6 g protein, 30 g carbohydrate, 3.5 g fat, 110 mg cholesterol, 65 mg sodium, 3 g fiber*

Diet Exchanges: *½ milk, 0 vegetable, ½ fruit, 1 bread, ½ meat, ½ fat*

2 Carb Choices

260 Calories

Slim Cherry Cheesecake

—Michelle King, St. George, Nebraska

"This is a light alternative to rich (almost too rich) and very fattening cheesecake (most use 3 or 4 bars of cream cheese). The taste is amazing! It's become a real favorite among my family and friends and I'm asked to bring it to almost every function we attend. One can indulge in a good-size piece without worrying about the fat or calorie content."

Prep time: 10 minutes
Chill time: 4 hours

CRUST

1½ cups graham cracker crumbs
¼ cup sugar
⅓ cup reduced-calorie, trans-free margarine, melted

FILLING

1 package (8 ounces) light cream cheese, softened
¼ cup sugar
1 teaspoon vanilla extract
1 container (8 ounces) light or sugar-free frozen whipped topping, thawed
½ package marshmallows (5 ounces)
1 can (20 ounces) light cherry pie filling

To make the crust: In a medium bowl, stir together the crumbs, sugar, and melted margarine. Press onto the bottom of a 9" springform pan. Refrigerate 15 minutes, or until chilled.

To make the filling: In a large bowl, mix with an electric mixer the cream cheese, sugar, and vanilla until smooth, about 2 minutes. Stir in the whipped topping and marshmallows. Spoon into the crust. Cover and refrigerate 4 hours, or until well chilled.

To serve, remove side of pan. Transfer cheesecake to a platter and spoon the cherry pie filling on top, letting it run over the edges.

Makes 12 servings

Per serving: *260 calories, 3 g protein, 41 g carbohydrate, 9 g fat, 5 mg cholesterol, 200 mg sodium, 0 g fiber*

Diet Exchanges: *0 milk, 0 vegetable, 0 fruit, 2 bread, ½ meat, 1 fat*

3 Carb Choices

140 Calories

Fresh Strawberry Pie

—Kim Cherichella, Lumberton, North Carolina

Prep time: 10 minutes
Cook time: 5 minutes
Chill time: 2 hours

1 box (3 ounces) sugar-free strawberry-flavored gelatin

3 tablespoons cornstarch

2 cups water

1 quart fresh strawberries, hulled and sliced

1 reduced-fat graham cracker pie crust (9" in diameter)

1 cup frozen fat-free whipped topping, thawed

In a medium saucepan, combine the gelatin and cornstarch, stirring to eliminate any lumps. Stir in the water and bring to a boil over medium heat, stirring. Cook and stir for 5 minutes, or until the mixture goes from cloudy to clear. Transfer to a large bowl, and let cool to room temperature (or refrigerate, stirring every few minutes to prevent jelling).

Set aside a small amount of strawberries for garnish. Fold the remaining strawberries into the gelatin mixture. Pour into the pie crust. Refrigerate for at least 2 hours, or until set. Decorate with dollops of whipped topping and the reserved strawberries.

Makes 8 servings

Per serving: *140 calories, 2 g protein, 24 g carbohydrate, 3.5 g fat, 0 mg cholesterol, 120 mg sodium, 1 g fiber*

Diet Exchanges: *0 milk, 0 vegetable, ½ fruit, ½ bread, 0 meat, 0 fat*

1½ Carb Choices

180 Calories

Hot Fruit

—Tanya Clapshaw, Vancouver, Washington

"Late-night snacking used to mean ice cream or butter-covered popcorn. But now I've found something with natural sweetness and wonderful flavor, and I feel as if I can indulge myself and feed my body, instead of depriving myself by dieting."

Prep time: 10 minutes
Microwave time: 4 minutes

1 **Granny Smith apple, cored and chopped**
1 **navel orange, peeled, and chopped**
1 **teaspoon ground cinnamon**
½ **cup fat-free vanilla yogurt**
2 **tablespoons pecan or walnut pieces**

Combine the apple, orange, and cinnamon in a medium microwaveable bowl. Cover with a lid or vented plastic wrap and microwave on high for 4 minutes, or until the fruit is hot and soft. Divide into 2 bowls, and spoon the yogurt evenly over each. Sprinkle with the pecans or walnuts and serve warm.

Makes 2 servings

Per serving: *180 calories, 4 g protein, 30 g carbohydrate, 5 g fat, 0 mg cholesterol, 35 mg sodium, 4 g fiber*

Diet Exchanges: *0 milk, 0 vegetable, 1 fruit, 1 bread, 0 meat, 1 fat*

2 Carb Choices

100 Calories

Splendid Baked Apples

—Dee Sanders, DeQueen, Arkansas

"This very simple and healthy snack is sure to satisfy any sweet tooth—and best of all, it's guilt-free!"

Prep time: 5 minutes
Bake time: 10 minutes

- 1 **Granny Smith apple, cored and cut into 6 wedges**
  Butter-flavored cooking spray
- 1 **tablespoon Splenda**
- ½ **teaspoon ground cinnamon**

Preheat the oven to 425°F.

Arrange the apple wedges, peel side down, in a small baking pan. Coat lightly with the butter-flavored spray. Sprinkle with the Splenda and the cinnamon.

Bake for 10 to 15 minutes, or until the apple wedges are tender and lightly browned.

Makes 1 serving

Per serving: *100 calories, 0 g protein, 29 g carbohydrate, 4.5 g fat, 0 mg cholesterol, 0 mg sodium, 3 g fiber*

Diet Exchanges: *0 milk, 0 vegetable, 1 fruit, 0 bread, 0 meat, ½ fat*

1 Carb Choice

210 Calories

Bananas Canadienne

—Laura Magill, Goodwood, Ontario, Canada

Prep time: 5 minutes
Bake time: 10 minutes

4 ripe medium bananas, peeled
2 to 3 tablespoons fresh lemon juice
½ cup pure maple syrup
   Thawed frozen fat-free whipped topping (optional)

Preheat the oven to 325°F. Coat a 13" × 9" baking dish with cooking spray.

Halve each banana lengthwise and place cut side up in the prepared baking dish. Drizzle with lemon juice to taste and spoon the maple syrup on top. Bake for 10 to 15 minutes, or until the bananas are hot, lightly browned, and glazed. Serve immediately, with whipped topping, if you like.

Makes 4 servings

Per serving: *210 calories, 1 g protein, 54 g carbohydrate, 0 g fat, 0 mg cholesterol, 0 mg sodium, 3 g fiber*

Diet Exchanges: *0 milk, 0 vegetable, 2 fruit, 1½ bread, 0 meat, 0 fat*

3½ Carb Choices

330 Calories

Rose's Coffee Cake

—Diana Harris, Portland, Oregon

Prep time: 15 minutes
Bake time: 55 minutes

2½ **cups unbleached all-purpose flour**
1½ **cups whole wheat pastry flour**
2 **teaspoons baking powder**
2 **teaspoons baking soda**
1½ **teaspoons salt**
2 **cups fat-free vanilla yogurt**
1 **teaspoon vanilla extract**
½ **cup granulated sugar + 1⅓ cups**
½ **cup chopped nuts**
¾ **cup reduced-calorie, trans-free margarine**
4 **large eggs at room temperature**

Preheat the oven to 350°F. Generously coat a 10" Bundt pan with nonstick cooking spray and dust with flour. Tap out any excess.

In a medium bowl, stir together the all-purpose and pastry flours, baking powder, baking soda, and salt. In another medium bowl, mix the yogurt and vanilla. In a small bowl, toss together ½ cup sugar and the nuts.

In a large bowl with an electric mixer at medium speed, beat the margarine and remaining 1⅓ cups sugar until light and fluffy. Add the eggs, one at a time, beating well after each.

With the mixer on low speed, beat in one-third of the dry ingredients, then one-third of the yogurt mixture. Repeat additions twice, mixing just until the batter is blended and smooth.

Evenly spoon half of the batter into the prepared pan. Sprinkle with the nut mixture. Top with the remaining batter, spreading it as evenly as possible.

Bake for 55 to 60 minutes, or until the cake shrinks from the sides and a wooden pick inserted in the center comes out clean. (If the cake is browning too fast, cover loosely with a sheet of foil.)

Let the cake cool in the pan on a wire rack for 30 minutes. Loosen the edges and turn out onto the rack to cool completely. Dust with confectioner's sugar, if desired.

Makes 16 servings

Per serving: *330 calories, 17 g protein, 51 g carbohydrate, 11 g fat, 55 mg cholesterol, 540 mg sodium, 2 g fiber*

Diet Exchanges: *0 milk, 0 vegetable, 0 fruit, 2½ bread, ½ meat, 2 fat*

3 Carb Choices

180 Calories

Summer Cooler Fruit Pie

—Lori Rael Northon, Auburn, Washington

"This is a heavenly light and refreshingly cool treat with endless flavor combinations. It completely satisfies my cravings for something sweet and luscious without piling on the calories."

Prep time: 5 minutes
Chill time: 2 hours 30 minutes

  1 **package (3 ounces) sugar-free lemon-flavored gelatin**

  1 **cup boiling water**

  1 **cup cold water**

  1 **container (6 ounces) fat-free lemon or vanilla yogurt**

  1 **teaspoon grated lemon peel**

  1 **container (8 ounces) frozen fat-free whipped topping, thawed**

1½ **cups fresh raspberries or blueberries**

  1 **reduced-fat graham cracker pie crust (9" in diameter)**

In a large bowl, combine the gelatin and boiling water, and stir until the gelatin is completely dissolved. Stir in the cold water. Whisk in the yogurt and lemon peel.

Refrigerate for about 30 minutes, or until the mixture begins to thicken. Fold in the whipped topping and berries. Pour into the pie crust. Cover and refrigerate for at least 2 hours, or until set.

Makes 8 servings

Per serving: *180 calories, 3 g protein, 28 g carbohydrate, 4 g fat, 0 mg cholesterol, 150 mg sodium, 2 g fiber*

Diet Exchanges: *0 milk, 0 vegetable, 0 fruit, ½ bread, 0 meat, 0 fat*

2 Carb Choices

110
Calories

Fruity-Cheesy Pizza

—Ben Hill, Dresden, Ontario, Canada

You can serve this for dessert or as a brunch dish.

Prep time: 15 minutes
Bake time: 8 minutes

 1 **package (10 ounces) refrigerated pizza dough**
 1 **container (8 ounces) part-skim ricotta cheese**
 1 **tablespoon grated lemon peel**
 1 **cup shredded part-skim mozzarella cheese**
 3 **large, ripe kiwifruits, thinly sliced**
 2 **cups sliced strawberries**
 ½ **cup halved seedless red grapes**
 3 **tablespoons sliced almonds**
1½ **tablespoons sugar**
 ¼ **teaspoon ground cinnamon**

Preheat the oven to 425°F. Coat a 15" × 10" rimmed baking sheet with nonstick spray.

Unroll the pizza dough on the prepared sheet. With your fingers, press the dough into a rectangle. Bake in the lower part of the oven for 8 to 10 minutes, or until golden brown.

In a small bowl, stir together the ricotta cheese and lemon peel. Spread over the pizza crust, and sprinkle with the mozzarella. Arrange the kiwi, strawberries, and grapes on the top. In a cup, mix together the almonds, sugar, and cinnamon, and sprinkle evenly over the fruit.

Bake about 5 minutes longer, or until the fruit is hot and the cheese has melted. Serve warm.

Makes 16 servings

Per serving: *110 calories, 5 g protein, 15 g carbohydrate, 4 g fat, 10 mg cholesterol, 170 mg sodium, 1 g fiber*

Diet Exchanges: *0 milk, 0 vegetable, 0 fruit, 1 bread, ½ meat, ½ fat*

1 Carb Choice

130 Calories

Vanilla Yolato

—Diana Harris, Portland, Oregon

Prep time: 5 minutes
Cook time: 25 minutes
Freeze time: 15 minutes

1 cup fat-free or 1% milk
½ cup sugar
1 tablespoon cornstarch
4 large eggs
1 cup low-fat vanilla yogurt
1 teaspoon vanilla extract

In the top of a double boiler, combine the milk, sugar, and cornstarch. Cook over simmering water, stirring almost constantly, for about 20 minutes, or until the mixture begins to thicken.

Beat the eggs with a wire whisk until light and foamy. Transfer the milk mixture to a large bowl. Gradually add the eggs, beating constantly. Pour the egg-milk mixture back into the double boiler. Continue to cook, stirring constantly, until the mixture coats the spoon and an instant-read thermometer inserted in the mixture registers 160°F. Do not let boil. Remove from the heat. Place the top of the double boiler in a large bowl filled with ice, and chill as quickly as possible.

When cold, whisk in the yogurt and vanilla. Freeze in an ice cream maker according to manufacturer's directions. Transfer to a freezer container, cover, and freeze until ready to serve.

Makes 8 servings, ½ cup each (1 quart)

Per serving: *130 calories, 6 g protein, 20 g carbohydrate, 3 g fat, 110 mg cholesterol, 75 mg sodium, 0 g fiber*

Diet Exchanges: *0 milk, 0 vegetable, 0 fruit, 1 bread, ½ meat, ½ fat*

1 Carb Choice

170
Calories

Mini Waffle Treats

—Sally Waggoner, Muncie, Indiana

"I love these easy no-bake treats. They're much cheaper than buying any of the popular frozen gourmet 'diet' ice cream sandwiches, and taste just as good."

Prep time: 10 minutes
Freeze time: 1 hour

1 box (7½ ounces) mini multigrain frozen waffles

¼ cup raspberry or strawberry sugar-free fruit spread

2 cups low-fat or fat-free frozen yogurt (any flavor)

Flaked coconut (optional)

Miniature chocolate chips (optional)

Sprinkles (optional)

Toast the waffles according to package directions. Cool. Spread each waffle with ½ teaspoon fruit spread. Top half of the waffles with 2 tablespoons frozen yogurt. Top the yogurt with the remaining waffles to make 16 mini sandwiches. Transfer to baking sheets and freeze for at least 1 hour.

If desired, roll edges in coconut, miniature chips, or sprinkles after freezing for 1 hour. Serve immediately or return to freezer until ready to serve.

Makes 8 servings, 2 treats each

Per serving: *170 calories, 5 g protein, 32 g carbohydrate, 1.5 g fat, 0 mg cholesterol, 150 mg sodium, 2 g fiber*

Diet Exchanges: *0 milk, 0 vegetable, 0 fruit, 1½ bread, 0 meat, 0 fat*

2 Carb Choices

120
Calories

Rice Crispy Cake

—Nadine Hill, Dresden, Ontario, Canada

"This makes an unusual dessert but appeals to the desire to chew! It takes time to consume . . . and each serving has only 10 grams of carbs and 42 calories. It gives me the opportunity to have a treat without blowing my diet. It is a case of having my cake and eating it too!"

Prep time: 10 minutes
Cook time: 5 minutes
Stand time: 1 hour

4 cups mini marshmallows
3 tablespoons trans-free margarine
1 tablespoon water
1 teaspoon vanilla extract
8 cups crispy rice cereal

Generously coat a 10" tube pan with cooking spray. In a large saucepan over low heat, combine the marshmallows, margarine, and water. Cook, stirring, until the marshmallows have melted. Remove from the heat and stir in the vanilla. Gradually add the cereal, mixing until well combined and sticky. With moistened hands, press the mixture into the prepared tube pan. Let stand for 1 hour. Unmold and cut into servings.

Makes 16 servings

Per serving: *120 calories, 1 g protein, 24 g carbohydrate, 2 g fat, 0 mg cholesterol, 180 mg sodium, 0 g fiber*

Diet Exchanges: *0 milk, 0 vegetable, 0 fruit, 1½ bread, 0 meat, ½ fat*

1½ Carb Choices

180 Calories

Chocolate Cheesecake

—Barbara Kohn, Whitewater, Wisconsin

"It helps me when dieting to watch my sugar level. If I have a sweet craving, I have a piece of this cheesecake with some fruit, and it satisfies me and keeps me away from chocolate that can make me fat again."

Prep time: 10 minutes
Bake time: 40 minutes
Chill time: Overnight

- ¼ cup toasted honey wheat germ
- 2 packages (8 ounces each) light cream cheese, at room temperature
- 1 container (8 ounces) firm tofu, well drained, softened
- ¾ cup granulated sugar
- ¼ cup Splenda
- 1 large egg, at room temperature
- 2 large egg whites, at room temperature
- 1 teaspoon vanilla extract
- 1 container (8 ounces) reduced-fat sour cream
- ⅔ cup unsweetened cocoa powder, sifted
- Assorted mixed berries and sliced melon for serving (optional)

Preheat the oven to 375°F. Coat a 9" springform pan with cooking spray. Dust the pan with the wheat germ, turning the pan to coat the sides and bottom evenly. Place the pan in the freezer while preparing the batter.

In a food processor, combine the cream cheese, tofu, sugar, and Splenda. Process until smooth and well blended, scraping down the sides of the bowl. Add the egg, egg whites, and vanilla; process until blended. Add the sour cream and cocoa; process until just blended.

Pour the cream cheese mixture into the prepared pan. Bake for 40 to 45 minutes, or until just firm near the center. Transfer to a wire rack to cool. Refrigerate cheesecake overnight. Serve with fresh fruit, if desired.

Makes 12 servings

Per serving: *190 calories, 10 g protein, 20 g carbohydrate, 9 g fat, 40 mg cholesterol, 170 mg sodium, 2 g fiber*

Diet Exchanges: *0 milk, 0 vegetable, 0 fruit, 1 bread, 1 meat, 1 fat*

1 Carb Choice

Chocolate Dreams

—Judith Michalski, Rochester Hills, Michigan

"I have a sweet tooth and am a chocoholic, too! When I get the urge for something sweet and chocolaty, I want a dessert that will satisfy both cravings. This soufflé-like dessert is best when eaten while still warm, with a little fat-free whipped topping slightly melted on top."

Prep time: 10 minutes
Bake time: 15 minutes

2 slices whole wheat bread, torn into small pieces

½ medium apple, cored and sliced thin or chopped, or 2 tablespoons unsweetened applesauce

1 tablespoon unsweetened cocoa powder

1 tablespoon low-fat or fat-free cottage cheese

2 teaspoons miniature chocolate chips

2 teaspoons Splenda

¼ teaspoon ground cinnamon

1 large egg white

¼ teaspoon cream of tartar

Preheat the oven to 350°F. Spray two 8-ounce custard cups with cooking spray.

In a medium bowl, stir together the bread, apple or applesauce, cocoa, cottage cheese, chocolate chips, Splenda, and cinnamon.

In another medium bowl, with an electric mixer at high speed, beat the egg white and cream of tartar until moist, fairly stiff peaks form when the beaters are lifted. Fold the beaten white into the bread mixture. Spoon evenly into the prepared custard cups.

Bake for 15 to 20 minutes, or until puffed, firm, and a wooden pick inserted in the center comes out clean. Let cool 5 minutes before serving.

Makes 2 servings

Per serving: *130 calories, 6 g protein, 23 g carbohydrate, 3 g fat, 0 mg cholesterol, 200 mg sodium, 4 g fiber*

Diet Exchanges: *0 milk, 0 vegetable, ½ fruit, 1 bread, ½ meat, ½ fat*

1½ Carb Choices

220 Calories

Berries in a Cloud

—Kathy Gruhn, New York, New York

"This is a delightful dessert that is both light and satisfying—and while it does contain sugar, there is no fat. For a flavor boost, toss the berries in some liqueur and let macerate for an hour or two before spooning into the meringue cups."

Prep time: 20 minutes
Bake time: 55 minutes

4 **large egg whites, at room temperature**
  Pinch of salt
2 **cups sugar**
2 **cups mixed seasonal berries**

Preheat the oven to 200°F. Line 2 baking sheets with parchment paper.

In a large bowl with an electric mixer at medium speed, beat the egg whites and salt until frothy. With the mixer at high speed, beat in sugar in a steady stream. Continue beating until whites stand in stiff, glossy peaks when beaters are lifted.

Spoon the meringue into a piping bag or large zip-top bag with a corner snipped off. Pipe 16 circles (4½" round) onto the parchment paper. Pipe 2 or 3 layers of meringue around each circle to make cups.

Bake the meringues about 55 minutes, or until dried out but not beginning to brown. Let cool for 2 to 3 minutes. Transfer to wire racks to cool completely. Spoon the berries into the cups just before serving.

Makes 8 servings

Per serving: *220 calories, 2 g protein, 55 g carbohydrate, 0 g fat, 0 mg cholesterol, 65 mg sodium, 1 g fiber*

Diet Exchanges: *0 milk, 0 vegetable, ½ fruit, 3 bread, 0 meat, 0 fat*

3½ Carb Choices

200 Calories

Fruit Mousse with Angel Food Cake

—Kim Tweed, Cape May Court House, New Jersey

Prep time: 15 minutes
Chill time: 1 hour 15 minutes

- 1 **prepared angel food cake (8 ounces), regular or sugar-free**
- 1 **package (12 ounces) unsweetened frozen strawberries or raspberries**
- ½ **cup sugar**
- 1 **envelope (.25 ounce) gelatin**
- ½ **cup cold water**
- 1 **container (8 ounces) frozen light whipped topping, thawed**

Cut the cake into 8 slices, sized to fit dessert dishes. Place the slices in the dishes and set aside.

In a medium saucepan over medium heat, combine the berries and sugar. Cook, stirring occasionally, 5 minutes, or until the berries are broken down and the sugar is dissolved. If desired, strain the mixture to remove seeds. (You should have about 1 cup.) Cover and refrigerate about 15 minutes, or until just lukewarm.

In a small bowl, sprinkle the gelatin over the water. Let stand about 5 minutes or until the gelatin is dissolved. Stir the gelatin into the fruit mixture.

Place the whipped topping in a large bowl. Fold one-half of the fruit mixture into the topping. Spoon the topping mixture over the cake slices. Cover and refrigerate about 30 minutes, or until set. Spoon the remaining fruit mixture over each dessert. Cover and refrigerate about 30 minutes, or until set with a smooth glaze.

Makes 8 servings

Per serving: *200 calories, 3 g protein, 42 g carbohydrate, 3.5 g fat, 0 mg cholesterol, 220 mg sodium, 1 g fiber*

Diet Exchanges: *0 milk, 0 vegetable, ½ fruit, 2 bread, 0 meat, 0 fat*

3 Carb Choices

It Worked for Me!

Evia Nelson

VITAL STATS

Weight lost: 35 pounds

Time to goal: About 1 year

Greatest challenge: Limiting carbs and sugar

Evia Nelson was 20 the spring she met her first husband, Charles. They were engaged by October and married the following July. Evia was the thinnest she ever was—weighing in at a mere 135 pounds—and it seemed as if a picture-perfect life had begun.

After the wedding, Charles worked nights, which meant Evia would come home to an empty house, with the television, soda, and chips as her sole companions. "Before I knew it, my marriage was unraveling—and my figure was ballooning." By the following February, they'd separated for good.

To ease the pain, Evia would shovel in whatever food seemed most soothing. "I'd speed-dial Papa John's and devour a large pizza and several beers. At first I didn't realize how much weight I was gaining, and by the time I reached 195 pounds, I just didn't care."

About a year and a half after the divorce, Evia stumbled on an article about an overweight woman who'd run a marathon. "Although it had been 3½ years since I'd last laced up my sneakers, I set a big goal for myself: running the May 2000 Pittsburgh Marathon." Giving herself 5 months to get in shape seemed the perfect kick-start to change.

Evia mapped out her training, starting with mile 1 and working up from there. "I was so terrified of failure that even when we had a blizzard—rare in Raleigh—I had a friend drive me to the gym in his Jeep so I could run."

Despite her rigorous training, the scale didn't budge. "My mounting frustration led me to a 12-week diet-and-exercise group that met once a week." In addition, they worked with a nutritionist and a personal trainer.

The nutritionist was able to show Evia exactly what was wrong with her diet. "She noticed that I was taking in enough calories to feed a team of elephants. I was eating three times the recommended serving size of pasta and drinking well over a cup's worth of sugar in my tea every day."

So Evia reduced her portions, added back healthy fats, increased her fiber intake, and swapped water for sweet tea, and she began to lose about half a pound per week.

That May, it took Evia 5 hours and 36 minutes to cross the finish line with her arms in the air. "I knew this was the first taste of a new passion."

Photography Credits

Front Cover

Mitch Mandel/Rodale Images

Back Cover

Mitch Mandel/Rodale Images

Interior

All recipe photos by Mitch Mandel/Rodale
  Images

© Comstock: Sports Icons: page 3

© Hilmar: pages 4, 8, 16, 18, 24

© BananaStock: Food Nutrition: page 5

© PhotoDisc: Fitness and Well-Being: page 6

© Stockbyte: New Resolutions: page 7

© Media Bakery: page 9

© PhotoDisc: Shopping List: pages 12, 15

© PictureQuest: page 14

© PhotoDisc: Objects: Food & Drink: page 19

© Kurt Wilson/Rodale Images: page 21

© Ed Landrock/Rodale Images: page 25

© Mitch Mandel/Rodale Images: pages 27,
  29, 32, 34

© Getty Images: page 33

© Artville: Dining/Duncan Smith: page 35

© Comstock: Holiday and Celebration Icons:
  page 36

© Brand X Pictures: Food Icons: page 37

© Campari tomatoes: page 40

© American Spoon Foods: page 84

© Pom Wonderful: page 95

© Crum Creek Mills: page 101

© Melissa's: page 126

© Heinz: page 134

© Maya Kaimel's Indian Simmer Sauces:
  page 169

© RiceSelect: page 188

© Pepperidge Farm: page 200

© Quaker Oatmeal: page 202

© Cuisinart: page 215

© King Arthur Flour: page 219

© Yoplait: page 220

Courtesy of Evelyn Gross: page 69

Courtesy of Jackie Dornblaser: page 76

Courtesy of Lauren Huff: page 81

Photos by Hilmar: page 111

Courtesy of Kim Bensen: page 129 (before
  photo)

Photo by Hilmar: page 129 (couple photo)

Courtesy of Carrie Nelson: page 154 (before
  photo)

Photo by Hilmar: page 154 (standing in field)

Courtesy of Tim and Evia Nelson: page 250

Photo by Hilmar: page 250 (walking the dog)

Index

Underscored page references indicate boxed text. **Boldface** references indicate photographs.

Conversion Chart

These equivalents have been slightly rounded to make measuring easier.

VOLUME MEASUREMENTS

US	Imperial	Metric
¼ tsp	–	1 ml
½ tsp	–	2 ml
1 tsp	–	5 ml
1 Tbsp	–	15 ml
2 Tbsp (1 oz)	1 fl oz	30 ml
¼ cup (2 oz)	2 fl oz	60 ml
⅓ cup (3 oz)	3 fl oz	80 ml
½ cup (4 oz)	4 fl oz	120 ml
⅔ cup (5 oz)	5 fl oz	160 ml
¾ cup (6 oz)	6 fl oz	180 ml
1 cup (8 oz)	8 fl oz	240 ml

WEIGHT MEASUREMENTS

US	Metric
1 oz	30 g
2 oz	60 g
4 oz (¼ lb)	115 g
5 oz (⅓ lb)	145 g
6 oz	170 g
7 oz	200 g
8 oz (½ lb)	230 g
10 oz	285 g
12 oz (¾ lb)	340 g
14 oz	400 g
16 oz (1 lb)	455 g
2.2 lb	1 kg

LENGTH MEASUREMENTS

US	Metric
¼"	0.6 cm
½"	1.25 cm
1"	2.5 cm
2"	5 cm
4"	11 cm
6"	15 cm
8"	20 cm
10"	25 cm
12" (1')	30 cm

PAN SIZES

US	Metric
8" cake pan	20 × 4 cm sandwich or cake tin
9" cake pan	23 × 3.5 cm sandwich or cake tin
11" × 7" baking pan	28 × 18 cm baking tin
13" × 9" baking pan	32.5 × 23 cm baking tin
15" × 10" baking pan	38 × 25.5 cm baking tin (Swiss roll tin)
1½ qt baking dish	1.5 liter baking dish
2 qt baking dish	2 liter baking dish
2 qt rectangular baking dish	30 × 19 cm baking dish
9" pie plate	22 × 4 or 23 × 4 cm pie plate
7" or 8" springform pan	18 or 20 cm springform or loose-bottom cake tin
9" × 5" loaf pan	23 × 13 cm or 2 lb narrow loaf tin or pâté tin

TEMPERATURES

Fahrenheit	Centigrade	Gas
140°	60°	–
160°	70°	–
180°	80°	–
225°	105°	¼
250°	120°	½
275°	135°	1
300°	150°	2
325°	160°	3
350°	180°	4
375°	190°	5
400°	200°	6
425°	220°	7
450°	230°	8
475°	245°	9
500°	260°	–